The Rebel Allocator

By Jacob L. Taylor

Library of Congress Cataloging-in-Publication Data

Name: Taylor, Jacob, L. author.
Title: The Rebel Allocator / Jacob L. Taylor
Description: Folsom, CA, 2018 | dba Five Good Questions
Identifiers: ISBN-13: 978-1-7326883-2-2 (paperback) | ISBN-13: 978-1-7326883-3-9 (ebook)
Subjects: Business, commerce, capitalism
Classification: HF, HB501

Contact: *fivegoodquestions@gmail.com*, @farnamjake1

Printed in the United States of America
Imprint: 5GQ

Book design by Jacob L. Taylor
10 9 8 7 6 5 4 3 2 1

First Edition

From the Author:

In his 1987 letter to Berkshire Shareholders, Warren Buffett wrote:

> *"The heads of many companies are not skilled in capital allocation. Their inadequacy is not surprising. Most bosses rise to the top because they have excelled in an area such as marketing, production, engineering, administration, or sometimes, institutional politics. Once they have become CEOs, they now must make capital allocation decisions, a critical job that they may have never tackled and that is not easily mastered. To stretch the point, it's as if the final step for a highly talented musician was not to perform at Carnegie Hall, but instead, to be named Chairman of the Federal Reserve."*

Capital allocation is the process of deciding how money is spent inside a company. It's easy to forget how critical it is to the success of any business. Yet somehow after years of searching, I never found a definitive resource for learning about effective capital allocation. Many outlined the problem, but few offered solutions for the practitioner. It was a glaring omission I was determined to fix. "Obsessed" might be the most apt word.

This book started life as a nonfiction. I invested years researching everything tangentially related to capital allocation, going down more rabbit holes than Bugs Bunny. I wanted to write a book about capital allocation done right. And if I'm being honest, my ego wanted me to write *the book.* I crafted a nonfiction book proposal and entertained offers from publishers who agreed this was fresh territory. *Yet something wasn't right.* Around the same time, a good friend who was my age died in a freak hiking accident. I was forced to reimagine what kind of book I would want to leave for my two young boys if I were to disappear tomorrow. That sobering thought changed everything.

A thousand little nudges from the universe convinced me I had to tell a story if I wanted this work to have a lasting impact. There's an idea that emotion is the glue that makes any lesson stick. I explored the emotional mechanics of storytelling, heroes' journeys, even screenplay writing. Thoreau said that the price of anything is the amount of life you exchange for it. If that's true, this has been an expensive book.

I can already hear you saying, "A fictional story about a dry subject like capital allocation? *What a terrible idea."* I got a healthy dose of raised eyebrows when I shared the concept with friends. "Just write a damn nonfiction book like everyone else," their eyes told me. Yet I couldn't ignore Ralph Waldo Emerson's words in *Self-Reliance*:

> *"There is a time in every man's education when he arrives at the conviction that envy is ignorance; that imitation is suicide; that he must take himself for better, for worse, as his portion; that though the wide universe is full of good, no kernel of nourishing corn can come to him but through his toil bestowed on that plot of ground which is given to him to till. The power which resides in him is new in nature, and none but he knows what that is which he can do, nor does he know until he has tried."*

This book is the plot of ground that I had to till. I hope the story helps you retain the lessons and broadens your understanding of an important subject. That would be success to me.

Your humble author,

Jake Taylor

Jacob L. Taylor
August 2018

P.S. This work is decidedly fiction. Although I've borrowed elements from my own experiences for color, I took *plenty* of literary license. If we meet in real life, please don't psychoanalyze me--I'm married to a Ph.D. psychologist, so I get enough of that at home already.

PROLOGUE

I creep into the hospital room and place the overpriced get-well flowers I just bought in the downstairs lobby on a table. I silently take a seat next to the bed. Medical equipment beeps metronomically in the background. *How does anyone sleep around here?* His face is sunken and more ashen than last time I saw him. He's going downhill fast. The inevitable seems right around the corner, and I can feel my throat harden with emotion. I blink a few tears from my eyes.

I reach toward the bed and gently touch the back of his hand. His skin feels like parchment paper, loosely stretched over his bones. His breathing is at least steady, but labored and rattling. I can't help but take a few deep breaths of my own to compensate, like when you watch someone trapped underwater in a movie.

Without opening his eyes, the old man says in a gravelly voice, "I thought you'd never make it."

I let out a cathartic laugh. "You ruined my vacation," I say.

"I know, I'm sorry. But we still have one lesson left."

You're probably guessing this old man is my grandfather. He's not; we aren't even related. Yet he's one of the most important people in my life. Before I explain how I came to be in a hospital holding his hand in the last days, perhaps hours, of his life, let's rewind the clock...

CHAPTER 1

I grew up middle class with "granola" parents. They met in college at an environmental protest. Saving the whales? Or was it the rainforests? *Doesn't matter.* It was love at first sight. They were high on righteous indignation. Probably more. I guess there are worse places to be conceived than the back of a Westfalia?

There was a lot of talk around the dinner table of *the man* and how he was keeping everyone down and callously destroying the planet. We were taught that capitalism was evil, man at his predatory worst. The nightly news brought daily reminders of crooked corporations into our living room.

My father was an attorney, which should have made the family financially comfortable. And it would have, had he not taken on so many pro bono cases. Environmental damage or unfair labor practices--he was a sucker for a sob story. He took them on free of charge.

Maybe you get what you pay for because he certainly didn't win them all. He'd torpedo his case by not letting go of an irrelevant point. Self-sabotaged, windmill-tilted, unable to get out of his own way. We never starved, but we were a long way from Park Avenue.

My mother was a dedicated volunteer for various environmental crusades. In the best case, this involved her working the phones to raise money. At least she could do that from home. Too often she was pulled to out-of-town rallies and protests. Causes always trumped bake sales and Little League games. She loved us, but her passion was clearly for saving the planet, not motherhood.

It would be too dramatic to call my brother and I feral, but we were no strangers to the latchkey. I became adept at forging my parents' signatures. Not out of malfeasance, just to grease the wheels of educational bureaucracy. I made a lot of excuses for their absences over the years.

My father and mother were both exceptionally principled. Yet there was a selfishness to their moralism. I'm sure they felt like they were trying to leave a better world than they'd found. A casualty of their principles was the missed blocking and tackling required for good parenting. I felt like a statue that was half-carved on the shelf while the artist worked on more pressing projects.

The carving they did do made for a square peg in a world of round holes. I unconsciously adopted my parent's inflexibility, getting into many easily-avoided conflicts at school. There's taking a stand, and there's just being obnoxious. My parents never really distinguished the two; I didn't either. (*Maybe a first-grader shouldn't throw away another student's tuna sandwich because it wasn't from a dolphin-safe source?)* I often felt like I didn't understand the world around me. I couldn't shake the gnawing feeling that I didn't belong.

I did okay in school. The academic side wasn't crushing, though I wasn't in the same universe as those truly gifted. My struggles were mostly social, and I lacked self-discipline. I was the kind of kid who spent countless hours holed up alone in his room creating a frame-by-frame reenactment of The Battle of Hoth. Echo Base needed saved from the Empire for the thousandth time way more than I needed to study for a big test. *Priorities, right?*

Upon graduation, I went to the closest state school that would take me. My grades qualified me for better universities, but I lied and said I liked the state school's campus better. It was objectively worse by any measure, except that it allowed me to maintain the level of mediocre effort to which I was accustomed. I didn't want to have to compete with more talented classmates. If I hamstrung myself, I'd never have to compare the *real* me to my peers and find myself lacking. Better to just limp around the JV track and leave the foot-race of life to the swift.

The way the financial aid shook out, the price tags wouldn't have been that different between the better schools and my "safe" choice. They were all going to require a crippling amount of debt. There are over one trillion dollars in student loans in the U.S. and I think I'm on the hook for about half of that. Like all people my age, I was assured I'd make it up through better pay the rest of my life. This social contract was an American birthright and as good as gold. I bought it hook, line, and sinker. *What a sucker.*

CHAPTER 2

I chose journalism as my major. The Fourth Estate was a noble calling, sure to earn my parents' approval. Their protests were about raising awareness of problems--wasn't that a journalist's prime directive? At least I'd have a better idea what the hell they were crusading about.

My sophomore year, one of my professors got me a job writing for the school's paper. It was your standard left-leaning university rag, written by self-important students too young and naive to grasp the complexity of what we were writing about. I loved it. For the first time, I felt like I *belonged.*

The paper's staff was a collection of castoffs and misfits like myself. We would stay up until all hours of the night, debating issues over greasy food, sporting even greasier hair. It was an echo chamber of "enlightenment."

Early in my sophomore year, my father landed a big case. A large medical manufacturer had produced faulty surgical meshing that harmed a lot of people, including one of my mother's close friends. After a lengthy trial and despite their obvious culpability, the company got off on some technicality. I was livid. All of the suspicions I was raised with about the grotesque nature of capitalism were confirmed when I saw real people being hurt. Why wasn't there anyone who could protect the little guy from these greedy corporations? *Is this the universe's idea of some sick joke?*

I hatched a plan. I added a business minor as a trojan horse to mask my infiltration of the system. I would be invited in as a business journalist to praise the self-proclaimed Masters of the Universe. It'd be too late when they realized I was there to expose their seedy underbelly and destroy the beast from within.

I pitched the newspaper editor on a regular column of exposés taking down nefarious companies. I was a modern-day muckraker shining a disinfecting spotlight on greedy, cigar-chomping executives. I called it, "The Evils of Capitalism." *I know, not very original.* There wasn't much of a travel budget for primary research, but you'd be surprised how broad the window into evil can be cracked open with simply the internet and a telephone. My regular columns became very popular with my fellow students who recognized the same corporate malfeasance and were happy someone was speaking up. It wasn't like I was Woodward or Bernstein, but I started to get a reputation on campus. I was proud to be known as fighting for the little guy.

My parents never taught me much about finances. Like all students, I would get daily credit card offers in the mail. I really wanted a big screen TV and the new video game system that had just come out. All the credit card companies wanted was an address to send the card to. *Match made in heaven!* I was working hard in school, didn't I deserve some niceties? I racked up a pile of consumer debt to sit atop my mountain of student loans. But you can't have a nice TV without surround sound. With a center channel. And a subwoofer. *Everyone knows that life-truth.*

CHAPTER 3

In the time leading up to graduation, I diligently worked my contacts and trolled job boards for a journalism opening. I just needed to get my foot in somewhere. My lack of prospects was comically bad. I didn't expect the *New York Times* to be knocking down my door, but there was nothing. I thought about starting my own website where I continued my muckraking articles, but I had no idea how to make any money off of something like that. Plus, I was the last person on the planet who would want to start their own business. In a panic, I researched grad school options as a way of deferring the harsh realities of life.

Debt repayment would have to wait as well. I was already receiving threatening phone calls and constant harassment through the mail from the credit card companies. They didn't just want my address to send a new card in the mail. They wanted a pound of my flesh known as minimum monthly payments. It didn't matter if I had a job or not, they weren't shy in asking. I was afraid to answer my phone and my stomach churned whenever I checked the mailbox. I couldn't make myself log in to see the crushing school loan balances and proposed payment options either. Deep down I knew it was my own fault, but I still felt taken advantage of by the credit card companies. Has anyone ever read all of the fine print and disclosures before signing? *I certainly wasn't going to be the first.*

A few weeks before graduation, there was a job fair on campus. I figured there wouldn't be much for a journalism major--who's ever seen the WaPo recruiting, at a measly state school no less? I had nothing better to do, so I wandered amongst the thicket of booths. The corporate pushers were there, dressed in snappy suits and fake Colgate smiles.

Businesses needed the blood, sweat, and tears of new recruits to keep the machine lubed. The beast's maw gaped for fresh meat.

One booth had a comely woman working out front. She was striking in her pencil skirt and perfectly coiffed hair, a real head-turner. I made my way over and pretended to peruse the company's brochures, hoping she'd talk to me. It was her job after all. Instead, I was intercepted by some jock frat boy working the same booth. His was no doubt selected to lure in the students of the finer sex with his trapezoidal physique. Was he even a real employee or just an out-of-work model doing the devil's bidding? *Sure, I'd love to hear more about your company, Chad. Thanks for asking.*

"What's your name?" Chad inquired.

"Nick."

"Hi, Nick. What's your major?"

"Journalism." Chad tried to hide his good-luck-with-that face. To his credit, he quickly recovered.

"Well, Nick, have we got an opportunity for you. This company is ahh--mazing. You're going to love it."

"What is it?" I asked.

"It's a private equity firm called Big Rock," he said.

"I'm not sure that's for me," I said. *I didn't tell him I didn't really know what private equity even meant.*

"It wouldn't hurt to at least apply, right? That is, unless you don't want to make $100,000... per year," Chad said in a hushed tone, like he was letting me in on a secret. "That's the *starting* salary for an analyst. Imagine how quickly you'll be able to pay off your student loans with that kind of money." *Ugh, it had been a pleasant seven minutes since I'd last panicked from the crushing gravity of my student loans.* Chad had clearly made this pitch before and knew the exact pain point to squeeze.

“One hundred… thousand?” I said. *Is it even legal to make that much in a single year?*

“Yep, and it goes up from there,” he said. “Big Rock is legit and everyone knows private equity is the future.” His pearly whites flashed with promise.

“Hmm… I guess it wouldn’t hurt to just put in my resume, right?” I said. “What’s the worst that could happen?”

“Exactly,” Chad said.

It’s funny how we don’t recognize many of life’s little forks after we’ve sailed right through them.

CHAPTER 4

I filled out Big Rock's application, expecting a better chance of being chosen by NASA to pilot the first craft to Mars. To my amazement, the phone rang not long after and it wasn't a debt collector. It was an HR rep from the company, and she wanted me to come in for testing and a possible interview. I about fell over.

The interview process was quite thorough, as you'd expect. I came in to Big Rock's office with a sea of other young people. We were all chasing the six-figure golden ticket. The first filter was a standardized aptitude test on a computer, after which I rejoined the herd in a plush waiting room. Everywhere I looked were well-dressed men and women, gleaming with the eye of the tiger. I knew I didn't have any edge in my father's schlumpy, hand-me-down suit. *Why is my tie twice as wide as everyone else's?* My spirits were deflating quickly. What was I even doing here? I didn't need this. I got up to leave.

Just as I spotted the exit, a representative appeared and called my name to come back. I had made it to the next round. Maybe I did have a chance?! I was informed the next section would include a psych screening. *Welp, thanks for playing.* No way I was making it through that filter with my unfortunate habit of putting my foot in my mouth.

I stayed on my best behavior, but I did answer the psych questions with as much honesty as I could muster. I figured that everyone else would be saying what they *thought* the company wanted to hear. My only chance was to zig with honesty when my competition was zagging to pander.

I found myself back in the waiting room where it had thinned out considerably. Eventually someone came out and called my name. It was time for the actual interview. *Maybe that whole honesty schtick had worked?*

My panel of evaluators didn't seem that much older than me. It was clear none of them wanted to be there. It was getting late in the afternoon and you could see visions of happy hour dancing in their heads.

The panel ran through its list of perfunctory questions. I answered with as much enthusiasm as I could summon, playing my part in this strange courting dance. I cracked a joke here and there, earning a few courtesy chuckles.

Before I knew it, they were standing up to shake my hand. It was over. As I was walking out, I overheard the beginning of their deliberations.

"Journalism? C'mon," one of them said.

"Dave did say he wanted diversity…" said another.

"That's not what he meant," said a third as the door closed. *Well, that was fun. That reminds me, I should pick up a Powerball ticket--better odds than getting this job that I don't even recall actually wanting.*

But maybe journalism *was* the diversity Dave meant after all. I got a phone call a few days later informing me that I was being offered one of the openings. When could I start?

Oh, snap. What do I do now? *And how do I tell my parents I'm going to work for the man?!*

CHAPTER 5

There's always a catch. I found in my offer letter that I'd be making nothing near what Career Fair Chad had promised. He technically told me the truth when he said an analyst starts at six figures. He failed to mention that I would be hired as a *junior* analyst at $30,000. It's better than nothing, but now what?

Should I keep looking for a non-existent journalism job? Hide out in grad school? Start my own investigative journalism website that would crash and burn? It started to feel like I *had* to take the Big Rock offer. Wasn't that my only real play to get out of crushing debt and finally start adult life? Besides, if all went well, I'd be promoted to analyst and be making six figures in no time. Then I would have the resources to make smarter decisions. I could keep looking for journalism jobs on the side while I faked my way through whatever "private equity" meant.

I would take the position. Now time for the serious phone call with my parents. I was sick with dread. Yet the conversation was not what I was expecting. No yelling at me for selling out. Nothing about me being a cog in the machinery of oppression. They seemed as preoccupied with their own stuff as ever. They were noticeably happy when I mentioned the starting salary. *Maybe they were just relieved to have dodged the boomerang of moving me back in with them?* There was a strange anticlimactic feeling that I couldn't square.

I'd find out later what was really going on.

CHAPTER 6

Life at Big Rock was a whirlwind compared to the lazy pace of college. *If this is what it's like to be an adult, then you can keep it.* But like all things, you get used to it and you find a new normal.

I can only recently explain to you what "private equity" actually means. Here's the simple version: they buy entire companies, make changes, and usually sell the company off to someone else after a few years and a couple coats of paint. Most private equity companies borrow a lot of other people's money to "acquire targets." Big Rock was no different. We're talking *billions* of dollars flowing around--almost incomprehensible amounts of money. It's weird how quickly you get numb to all the zeros.

When private equity "makes changes" at a company, there's a wide spectrum of what that means. On one end is being an owner of the business. Investing in assets and people, coaching existing management, paying down debts, and improving operations. Think of a white knight riding in to slay the dragons. The hero saves the day and makes everything in the kingdom right again.

On the other end of the spectrum is behaving more like a short term renter--a squatter even. Getting control, selling off assets, stripping down the workforce to a skeleton crew, downsizing previous management, adding debt, and hollowing out operations. It's pillage and plunder with a thin veneer of civility. All of these actions create a one-time surge in profits. Everything looks better, for a while. Not an issue if you find someone to sell to before it all turns into a pumpkin. This style of private equity is like someone who undergoes heavy doses of plastic surgery. It may look better in the short term, but eventually it all deflates and starts to look wonky. Big Rock was on this short-term-renter side of the spectrum. In fact, they were one of the best-known plastic surgeons in the business.

What does a junior analyst do, you ask? I would gather information, clean up data sets, read and summarize research, help write reports, fetch coffee. I did whatever the real analysts wanted me to do. The goal was to find fat target companies that needed Big Rock's special touch and send those ideas up the chain of command for others to take the credit. I felt like a scout surveying the countryside for where to next send the ravenous horde.

Whoever *Diversity Dave* was, he may have actually been onto something. My background in journalism was proving handy. My internet sleuthing skills were well-honed and my report writing had a crispness that others lacked. I was used to writing under a deadline for the newspaper; this felt mild by comparison. The problem was there was so much financial jargon. Probably no surprise, but my business minor didn't prepare me for any of this. Everyone was speaking a foreign language. I'm surprised I didn't strain my neck from all the vacant nodding I did. *Amortization, synergies, ebi-what-da-eff-are-you-talking-about?* Can't we speak plain English? Is time so short that we really need an acronym for everything?

I did not fit into Big Rock's locker room culture. My stomach did flips when I imagined coworker interactions. I felt like I was wearing a mask at all times. I contemplated getting a service animal to cope with my anxiety, but figured it'd only draw more attention and harassment. *Nice parakeet, Nick.*

There was one person who made my life especially difficult. I'm not sure why this guy appointed himself my personal Biff Tannen, but he relished the role. His name was Vance. He had a flair for making my Big Rock experience creatively unpleasant. He was hired about six months before me, so maybe it was just "good-natured" hazing. I was the punchline of every joke. My favorite was an autographed picture of a shirtless Justin Bieber that kept appearing on my desk. *Thanks, Vance.*

Vance was everything I was not: tall, handsome, confident, smooth in speech, dapper in dress, socially adept. He was the crown prince of Big Rock and entitlement personified. He came from a well-to-do family and the rumor was it required one sizeable donation to get him into Harvard, and a second lump sum to get him out the door with a degree in marketing. He was now pursuing his MBA while he worked at Big Rock. *Overachiever.* Who knows what donations were required for the MBA, but he was ready to ascend the privileged throne of his choosing. He could have been the missing Winklevoss triplet.

I remember turning the corner in the break room and overhearing him talking to some coworkers around the watercooler about that weekend's sexual escapades in sordid detail. *They were both models? C'mon, Vance. Born on third base and thought he hit a triple.* I could only wonder what that was like.

I'm just self-aware enough to admit that I was jealous. Like crazy, Hulk-smash jealous. Who wouldn't be? He had everything. I also saw a lot of unscrupulous behavior. Changing numbers on reports to get the "right" results. Taking credit for work that wasn't his. Liberal abuse of the expense account. He wasn't abnormal for Big Rock's bro culture; he was just so brazen about it. At least the others made an effort to be sort of sly.

It felt like the rules didn't apply to him, and he knew it. Little did I know we were on a collision course.

CHAPTER 7

After surviving just shy of one year on the job, I was interrupted from my usual grind by my phone ringing. It was an HR representative informing me I had to report to a certain conference room. I wondered if I should start packing a parting-gift cardboard box with office supplies now. *The jig was up.*

I found my way to the conference room through a sea of cubicles. The man from HR was there with a director who was two or three levels above me. It looked bad. Even though I technically reported to this director, I was pretty sure he couldn't have picked me out of a lineup to save his life. *I guess his management style was more "decentralized"?*

"Hi...," the HR guy said glancing down at his paperwork to find my name, "... Nick. Have a seat."

"Am I in trouble?" I blurted. My mind was already racing.

"No," my boss said. "Well, maybe." They both laughed awkwardly. I didn't join them.

"Let's get down to brass tacks," Mr. HR continued. "The note that keeps coming up on your evaluations is that you need to catch up on your understanding of business to be a more effective analyst. We know you studied journalism in school, but we thought you'd be able to ramp up your business acumen more quickly than this."

"We really do need you to improve," said the boss. *How did he know? I doubt he'd read anything I'd ever written.*

"Ok…" I trailed off.

"But naturally, we can't have you learning everything on Big Rock's dime," said Mr. HR. The boss just nodded. "We suggest you apply to grad school and get your MBA after hours. There's a working professional program that should allow you to continue your duties at BR. If you get accepted, we'll keep you on in your junior analyst role. And if you make it all the way to graduation, you'll be a likely candidate to move up the ladder." He smiled like he'd just bestowed a splendid gift upon me. "But obviously, no guarantees." *Obviously.*

"What happens if I apply and don't get in?" I asked. I knew I was a journalist masquerading in the business world. Any MBA program would peg me as a phony straight away.

"We'll have to go in a different direction," my boss said. *I love the euphemisms of corporate speak.* "The good news is, they are taking applications now. If you hurry, you can take the GMAT and then apply. Your coworker, Vance, is halfway through the program. Maybe he can put in a good word for you?" *Yeah, I bet he'd be happy to.* I figured it'd be a bad idea to ask what the GMAT was at this point.

"OK, thanks," was all I could muster. I returned to my desk in a daze.

It turns out the GMAT is like the SATs, but for business school. Most people study for at least six months before they take the test. The more perfectionist types will spend over a year. *I had six days.* I ran to the closest bookstore and grabbed an armful of study guides. As I thumbed through them, my mood sank. This test would be impossible. *Well, we had a good run. Would they notice if I stopped showing up to work?*

With a healthy dose of diffidence, I submitted my application and started cramming around every waking moment, and even a few when I wasn't awake. I was studying for my life, or at least it felt that way. I'd be lying if I said not wanting to be shown up by Vance wasn't also a motivation. *Why should he get everything?*

I was fast-tracked to interview with the school before taking the GMAT. Everything went well enough with the interview. The usual standard questions and answers. Smile and nod here. Funny anecdote there. Hearty handshake, pump one-two-three. The school informed me that if I scored well enough on the GMAT, I was in.

I'd never taken a standardized test that determined if I would wind up homeless or not. As you can imagine, it was rather motivating. The admissions board required me to get a 650 or higher. That would put me in the upper 75th percentile of test takers, no small feat on such short notice.

On the morning of the GMAT, I had to pull over on the way to the testing center to vomit in the bushes. And again in the bathroom when I got there. *Don't worry, I knew I'd be a mess and built the time into my schedule.* Why was I so nervous? I didn't even want an MBA. But the thought of being destitute scared me. I needed this Big Rock job and the eventual money I'd be making. *So. Much. Damned. Debt.*

I finished the test feeling strangely invigorated. I gave it my best effort, and I felt I had done reasonably well... but 650 was such a high hurdle. I secretly put the odds as a coin-flip; it would be close. I started compiling a mental list of overpasses I might someday inhabit. *Oh, that one looks quaint, though a bit drafty in winter.*

Two weeks later, I got a call from the school. They had received my GMAT results. *Gulp.* I had scored a 700, putting me in the 90th percentile. *What?!* They were pleased to offer me admission in the fall.

Wow, I was going to business school. Maybe I wasn't destined to be living in that van down by the river just yet? I didn't know it then, but business school would provide me the lucky break that would change my life forever.

CHAPTER 8

The leaves changed colors, signaling for school to start. I thought between work and school that Vance and I would have enough commonalities to start getting along. Maybe even bond? I was wrong. I remained his social fulcrum. He made jokes at my expense to elevate his status in this new group, with the added bonus of lowering mine. I guess leopards don't change their spots, regardless of the environment.

I did make one new friend at business school. His name was Larry and he was a bowling ball of a man. He was the starting nose tackle for his college football team, though that had been a few years and countless cheeseburgers ago. He grew up country strong on a farm moving hay bales around before breakfast. He now owned his own business where he did appraisals of industrial equipment. It seemed to fit his country personality. He was back in school to learn more valuation techniques and to figure out how to take his business to the next level. His words--I honestly wasn't sure what he hoped to accomplish.

Larry and I became friends because we were both a little socially awkward. Like two castaways stranded on a deserted island, it was easier to survive as a pair than solo. It didn't take long for Vance to pounce. "Look everyone, it's Nick and the Fat Man." *Ummm, wasn't the show called, "Jake and the Fat Man," dummy?*

The irony was not lost on me that it's wasn't that long ago that I had been trying to make a name for myself in the journalism world by taking down *the man*, and now I was spending my nights and weekends to *become him.* Packing away my anti-capitalist sentiments was a matter of survival. When you're in a room full of blood-thirsty economic savages, it's best to just keep your mouth shut and avoid drawing unwanted attention. *Keep your friends close...*

My hope was that business school would be a magic decoder ring for my work at Big Rock. Suddenly, everything might make sense. This was not the case. In many ways, I was more confused than ever--like if you handed a foreigner a dictionary and expected them to just suddenly be fluent. Work and school kept me brain-numbingly busy. I just kept putting one foot in front of the other as I wandered through the wilderness of young adulthood.

At the end of my first semester, there was a drawing at school to travel to the Midwest to meet some billionaire captain of industry. Everyone was in a big stir over the chance at a Q&A session that was sure to lead to their own fortune. Or at least a lucrative job offer. I figured this guru was more likely to fleece them than to teach them to get rich. How else do you become a billionaire if not by seizing every opportunity for gain? *That's just math.*

In the name of conformity, I threw my name into the school's drawing. I didn't want to win, so I was happy the odds were so long. Then something weird happened. *I actually won.* I was miraculously selected to travel to Wichita, Kansas and meet the billionaire.

It dawned on me this could be a golden opportunity. With special insider access, I could write my ultimate take-down piece. He'd never suspect a thing coming from an innocuous, wet-behind-the-ears student. It might even be just the ticket to catapult myself into a real career in journalism. As an added bonus, I'd have company: Larry also won.

But guess who didn't win? Vance! He still managed to get his shot in. "What's that old geezer going to teach you? He'll probably be dead before you even make it out there. Nothing worthwhile is happening in a flyover state like Kansas anyway."

Stay classy, Vance.

CHAPTER 9

It wasn't long before February brought my Wichita trip. I was up before the sun to catch an early departure. After a smooth, homework-filled flight, I stepped off the plane and climbed the jetway. The airport carpet was brown and shiny from years of foot traffic. The paint on the walls was just on the verge of peeling. Tiny by most airport standards, I quickly made my way outside only to be stopped for a loss by a stinging cold wind in my face. I was a long way from home in sunny California. Dirty piles of plowed snow blighted every line of sight. *Welcome to winter in Wichita.*

I hailed a cab and made my way to the hotel where I was to be sardined together with Larry. I opened the hotel room door to survey the situation. *Damn, looks like Larry and I would be sharing a single bed this evening.* If anything, Larry had only added weight since starting school. *Stress-eating much?* The scene from the film "Trains, Planes, and Automobiles" spooled up in my mind. *Mental note for later: keep your hand from between the two pillows!* Settling into the room and awaiting snuggle-time with my John Candy, I ironed my dad's suit that I had permanently borrowed and daydreamed about what tomorrow would be like. Finishing my chores, I piled up the pillows and threw myself onto the bed to watch some mindless hotel TV.

I awoke to the click of the door unlocking. Larry lumbered into the room like a grizzly. I saw him doing the math on the sleeping arrangements and we shared a bemused eyebrow raise.

"I'm starving--let's eat!" Larry announced in predictable fashion.

We walked into the quaint downtown district and I had some of the best BBQ of my life. Wanting to be fresh for the morning, we called it an early night and headed back to the hotel room to get comfy.

The next morning I awoke early, throwing Larry's heavy arm off of me. I showered and choked down a cup of burnt coffee in the lobby, waiting for my classmates to join me. I caught a brief reflection of myself in a window. I was literally parading in my father's Sunday best--*what a joke.* Stepping outside the hotel, it looked like a cold, normal Tuesday in Wichita with people going about their Midwestern lives.

The small group of winning students and two faculty chaperones boarded a small bus and made our way from the hotel. After a short drive, we arrived at an unremarkably beige fifteen-story building. *Are we sure this is it?* Unimpressive would be putting it mildly. *This was the secret lair of a billionaire? Where's the money bin?* Our group gathered our belongings and started exiting the bus. *I guess we're here.*

I glanced across the parking lot and noticed an odd scene. A half-dozen or so obviously homeless people were gathering around the back of a late model Cadillac. The trunk popped open and an old man in a suit exited the driver's side. He went to the back and started passing out red and white paper bags to each person. The homeless dug into their bags, revealing McMuffins and hash browns. Maybe he was the billionaire's chauffeur? There was a shared jovial body language; a comfort like it happened every day just like this. Before I could see how this odd scene would evolve, we were herded into the beige building.

It took a few trips for the elevator to shuttle our group to the fourteenth floor. We were led into a medium-sized conference room. Inside was a standard conference table with chairs around it. At one end of the table stood a podium. We took our seats around the table, the overachievers jockeying for spots closest to the podium. A quiet din of small-talk filled the room while we waited.

A hush spread over us as an elderly man in a dark suit shuffled his way inside and stood in front of the podium. *The chauffeur?* What was he doing here? It took an embarrassingly long time for me to put the pieces together. The chauffeur feeding the homeless *was our billionaire. Huh?*

He was slightly above average in height, and thin. Still fancying myself an investigative journalist, I looked for clues about the man. His gait was slow and methodically ginger, signaling his advancing years. Yet there was an easy confidence to him, like he'd seen it all before. Based on his facial features, he was probably handsome in his youth. His shock of hair was a mixture of gray and white and thinning in the front. It was surprisingly disheveled. I guess at some age you stop caring about what your hair looks like and move on to more important things. *Like swimming in your money bin. Or feeding the homeless out of the back of your car.* Maybe I didn't have this guy pegged just yet.

"One billion, two billion, three billion," he said, jokingly testing the microphone affixed to the podium. The financial magazines had several pet names for him: "The Rebel Allocator" or "The Wizard of Wichita." But his Christian name was Francis Xavier, and I relished my role as David, preparing to take down Goliath.

CHAPTER 10

Standing at the podium, Mr. Xavier scanned the room and looked at each one of us individually. He didn't smile. Instead, he began with some prepared remarks.

"I don't want any of you here," he said. "It's a waste of my time. You all were already given every advantage you'd ever need in life." *Whoa, not the start I was expecting--this was going to be easier than I thought.* He wasn't done. "You don't need any more handouts. But my assistant thinks it's is good for my image to talk to students, and she keeps the trains running on time, so here you are." We exchanged bewildered looks.

"I have a few things to pass along, not that today's generation will likely understand... never worked an honest day in their damned lives," he grumbled. "Then I imagine you'll want to bother me with questions before you stare at your phones while I answer." *Hmm...*

"First, for seventy-seven years now, I've tried to go to bed a little smarter than I woke up. Constant improvement is the only way to succeed. It makes what is difficult to achieve become inevitable. Success is a few simple disciplines, practiced daily. Failure is simply a few errors in judgment, repeated daily."

"Second, the most important decision I ever made was choosing whom to marry. Nothing will have a bigger impact on your life than your spouse. I got very lucky in this department. Keep your eyes wide open before you get married..." He trailed off, then said with a wink, "Then keep them a little closed after you tie the knot." The group laughed nervously. *Maybe he wasn't a total curmudgeon?*

"Third, a lot of people ask me what I look for when I hire someone, besides blonde hair and shapely curves," he winked again. "I'm only kidding... I prefer brunettes." *Is this a geriatric standup routine?*

"Here's the real answer," he said, now serious. "There are three qualities you want: integrity, intelligence, and energy. If you don't have the first, the other two can kill you. If you hire someone without integrity, you really want them to be dumb and lazy." Everyone chuckled as you could feel the room loosening up.

Mr. Xavier kept rolling. "It is remarkable how much long-term advantage I've found by trying to be consistently *not* stupid. You should try it sometime. Instead of aiming to be very intelligent, just don't be a dumbass. If you avoid most of the big mistakes, you don't have to be that smart to succeed." *Good news for us dumbasses of the world.*

"Fourth," he said. "As you probably know, I've done pretty well for myself financially. You're capable of doing the same. Probably not as well, but good enough. It's a simple recipe: consistently spend less than you earn. Automatically tuck away ten percent of whatever you make. You don't even have to be an investment genius with that ten percent. You will have a staggering amount of money by the time you're my age with even a modest level of compounding. I probably should have saved the secret to getting wealthy for last as you all look ready to leave to go make your fortunes." He smiled--it was becoming clear that his gruff act at the beginning might be a ploy to grab our attention. *The old man was wiley--game on.*

"You'll find that once you're wealthy, it isn't as big a deal as you thought. Like losing your virginity. I will say that the freedom it affords is nice. I don't mind avoiding the roving hands of the TSA." He paused to gather himself, "Number five, I have a proposition for you. No, it's not of the indecent variety. Besides, none of you look like Demi Moore." *His jokes were dated, but not that bad.*

"Here's your deal: I'll buy each of you whatever car you want. Right now. Mercedes, Ferrari, Chevy, whatever your heart desires. Who's in?" Naturally, everyone raised their hands and started daydreaming like a kid in line to sit on Santa's lap. "But there's a catch," he added. "You have to drive that same car for the rest of your life. No matter what, that's your car from here on out." At first blush, driving a fancy sports car for the next eighty years didn't sound that bad, except for the disgusting consumerism message it would send. I also realized I couldn't even afford the insurance and maintenance for a car like that. It'd be up on blocks and I'd be riding the bus within a year.

"If you could only have one car for eternity, how carefully would you drive? You wouldn't want to crash it, right? You would wash and wax your car all the time to make sure the paint didn't peel off. You would take it in for regular maintenance to keep it purring. You would only use premium gas." We all nodded. "Well, I hate to break it to you, but you're already part of a Faustian bargain like this. Except your car is made of meat." *What?* The nodding had stopped. Anticipating our confusion, he said, "I'm referring to your body. Barring some miraculous advances in medicine, you're only going to get one body in this lifetime. Don't crash it. Take it in for regular maintenance. Give it premium fuel. Don't let it just sit in the driveway and rot. Wash it and wax it, metaphorically speaking... but also literally if that's what floats your boat." He chuckled at his own dirty joke. *I might actually be starting to like this Mr. Xavier. Stay objective, Nick...*

"I feel a little sorry for this younger generation," he said. "You have access to so much easy information and entertainment. It's truly the best of times and the worst of times. With all of the electronic gizmos, there's an overwhelming temptation to multitask. I'm not sure I would survive if I were you. I don't have the willpower. I can see it in your faces that you're dying to get on your phones and check the latest celebrity gossip. Here's what my strategy would be if I were you: we each only have twenty-four hours in a day, no matter what's in our bank account. What we focus on is what differentiates us. Every morning, ask yourself this question: 'What's the *one* thing I could work on today that if I did a good job, it would make everything else easier, or maybe even unnecessary?' Keep four hours carved out of your calendar to work on that *one* answer. Make it sacred time with no interruptions. Put everything else away, including your phone and whatnot. Focus deeply during that four-hour stretch at making progress on your most important thing. I can guarantee you a huge advantage in life if you do this. Unfair even. Most people overestimate what they can get done in a day, but radically underestimate what they can get done in a month… in a year… in a decade, with four hours of dedicated work. You could goof off the rest of the day and still run circles around your peers. At least that's been my experience."

"Next topic. I have a firm belief, some may even call it bias, that one of the oldest technologies is still the best for the spread and absorption of information. It's called 'a book.' Have you ever heard of it?" he asked. *Who has time to read books these days, old timer?*

"Raise your hand if you read more than five books last year," he said. Everyone raised their hand. "Keep them up if you read more than ten books." Hands started dropping. "Fifteen?" Most had fallen by now. "OK, you are probably in the minority. The statistics say the average is about four books per year. At least that's what people report. I bet it's lower. They might *start* four books per year." *He was probably right--my nightstand was a shrine to literary false starts.*

"Think about the return on investment a book offers. For around ten dollars, you get to have an in-depth conversation with an expert who dedicated years to distilling all the information about a topic. For the cost of a mediocre dinner, you get access to years of another human's effort. I did the math. If it took the author one year of work, you're paying them about one penny *per hour*. How much time does this penny-per-hour investment save you in culling through information? We're talking lifetimes." *That is a pretty good deal.*

"I like to think of books as the 'oil of information.' You all probably think oil is evil, but it's actually a blessing. We'd all be sitting around a campfire in loincloths right now without oil. About twelve thousand gigawatt-hours of solar energy hits the earth every day. That's a lot of energy, but the problem is, it's spread out over two hundred million square miles of the earth's surface. Nearly all life makes a living collecting and processing that solar energy in different ways. Plants and animals are just collections of this energy, and sometimes they get trapped underground and subjected to extreme geological pressures. The decayed material becomes so compacted for so long that it's eventually smashed together enough to become oil. In essence, oil is made up of millions of years of concentrated sunlight. Did you know that oil has ten times the energetic density of a stick of dynamite? Thank God for oil. It gives us the energy to create the modern world." *It was also the reason for wars in the Middle East, crushing autocratic governments, and destroying Mother Nature with smog.* I swallowed hard to not engage him in debate. I needed to stay patient. *Step into my parlor...*

Mr. Xavier rolled on, "Instead of energy, books are an extreme concentration of information. Oil is formed under Herculean pressures inside the Earth. The human equivalent of that amount of mental pressure is applied to the information that becomes distilled into a book. Mankind has been able to raise living standards immensely by harnessing better energetic materials. First we burned dung, then wood, then coal, and then oil. Books are simply a better fuel substrate for our brains. And

I'm sorry if that didn't fit into 140 characters." *The old man's prepared spiel was good, I'll give him that.*

"So long story short," he said. "Read a damn book once in awhile. You'll be the better for it, and maybe we won't have a world full of dumbasses."

I hated to admit it, but in a world of political correctness, I found Mr. Xavier's authenticity magnetic. We were hanging on his every word.

CHAPTER 11

My classmates were hurriedly scribbling notes as Mr. Xavier spoke. He was sharing decades of insights--we'd be fools not to write down every word. And yet, I hadn't cracked my notebook.

"Young man," the old man said, his eyes homing in on me. "Everyone else is taking notes. Is there a reason you're not?"

My blood ran cold. I looked around at my classmates for help, finding only narrowed eyes of judgment. *Damn, he must have sniffed out my plot to take him down. But how?*

"Well, sir..." I stammered. "The thing is... in undergrad I studied journalism. I used to take a lot of notes when doing interviews. One of my professors who was a seasoned journalist saw me in action and pulled me aside. He told me I should never take notes when conducting an interview. Record it, sure, but look your subject in the eye when they're speaking. He told me if you want the other person to open up and share their story, they need to feel like you're part of the conversation. If it feels like an interrogation, they'll measure every word. Also, if you're taking notes, it distracts you from empathizing. You won't find the spark that leads to the next insightful question." I was on a bit of my own roll now. "Lastly, most people never go back through their notes anyway. If it's that important, it'll find its way back into your head. Since that conversation, I've taken notes sparingly. Plus, I didn't think we were allowed to record this." *That outta throw him off my trail.*

My classmates sheepishly put down their pens, unsure of what they should do next to maintain social decorum. Mr. Xavier slowly nodded and continued to stare at me, his wheels turning. *Were guards about to swarm and drag me to a privately-funded capitalist dungeon?*

"Fair enough," he finally said, "and a nice segue into my last point to share." Mr. Xavier never broke eye contact with me. "Throughout your life, you should follow your own *inner scorecard*. What does that mean? Don't spend a lot of time worrying about what other people think of you. Progress is only accomplished by those who are stubborn and a little weird. It's easier said than done, but if you stay true to your own principles and follow your own inner scorecard, it's your best shot at happiness. That's how I got the nickname "The Rebel Allocator." I'm done. Now it's your turn to ask me a series of bonehead questions." He smiled teasingly.

It dawned on me that my growing affinity toward Mr. Xavier might have been because he seemed comfortable as an outsider. He embraced his rebel persona. It gave me hope that being an outcast might be a stepping stone to something better. But first, I hoped my fellow classmates would ask the old man some thoughtful questions. *You have to dig pretty deep to find the soft underbelly.*

CHAPTER 12

Mr. Xavier abandoned the podium and took his position at the head of the table with us. You could tell this was his normal seat when in this room.

"Alright," he said after settling in as old men do. "Now's the time for you to ask me some questions if you want. Who's first? And by the way, you can call me 'Mr. X' for short. That's what everyone calls me around here."

A bubbly overachiever predictably raised her hand. "I'll go first, Mr. X. How did you end up in the restaurant business? And why hamburgers? They seem so… like, you know... gauche. I should preface that I'm a vegan." She looked around for kudos. *Oh, brother.*

Mr. X gave us a smile that hinted at nostalgia and pain. "It's a bit of a long story, but since you asked... I was the first-born in my family, at the dawn of the Great Depression. My parents were struggling to survive as farmers in the northern tip of Texas. In the mid-1930s, there was a severe drought. Have you ever heard of the Dust Bowl? Ever read *The Grapes of Wrath*?" We nodded, but he acted like he didn't believe us. "You've never seen anything like it in your lifetimes. You've grown up as pampered snowflakes, never missing a meal." Harsh, but maybe a little fair looking around the room. *-cough-Larry. -cough-*

"People were literally starving," Mr. X said. He had a dark look in his eyes. "It was a very difficult time. Farming in Texas was a dead end, and my father started searching for other work. We moved to Wichita where we had family scratching out a living. My father was too fiercely independent to take a job working for someone else, but all he knew was farming and food. His favorite meal was the hamburger, so he decided to make a go of it by opening his own hamburger stand. Not everyone knows the backstory, but my father called it 'Cootie

Burger' because my parents were childhood sweethearts and my mother used to tease him that he had cooties. It became her pet name for him--a term of endearment. I've personally never liked it. Who wants cooties on their food? But that's where 'Cootie Burger' came from." I had been wondering the origin of such a weird name.

"Anyway, as I said, the country was struggling economically. Many couldn't afford food, let alone going out to eat. We barely scraped by. Along came two girls after me and one of them contracted polio, adding to our hardship. It was ironic that we owned a restaurant, yet felt like we never had enough to eat. At its worst, we lived in the back storeroom, hiding our bedding from customers. I remember having one pair of socks. With holes in them. The good news was, I never lost them in the dryer. They were always on my feet!" He laughed heartily at his own joke. I tried to imagine for myself what it must have been like for Mr. X's father. The struggle of being surrounded by food every day, but barely able to feed his family. Like Tantalus from Greek mythology, his eternal punishment to stand beneath a fruit tree, the food ever eluding his grasp.

"We couldn't afford employees, so the whole family worked in the restaurant. It sounds dismal, but I wouldn't trade that time for anything. That crucible made us fiercely loyal to each other and gave us the grit to become who we were. My father swore he was the first to put a fried egg on top of a burger. He was hungry one morning and there happened to be one egg left in the house. He threw it on a leftover burger and the rest is Cootie history. Out of hardship came innovation. It seems like a small thing, but it was enough to make our little restaurant stand out just enough stay afloat. And now it's an American staple."

"Was it snowing *and* uphill both ways?" one of the chaperones jumped in, trying to be funny.

Mr. X eyed her briefly before answering. "It felt that way sometimes. Fast forward a few years. I did well in school; I felt like I had to after seeing my parents' sacrifice. I earned a scholarship to Oklahoma State to study engineering. The country had recovered economically after the War, but my family's prospects had stagnated. The restaurant business is tough. My plan was to get through school as fast as possible and find employment so I could send a financial lifeline to my struggling family." I pictured a young Mr. X as a mountain climber; his family trapped down in a crevasse awaiting rescue. What pressure for a nineteen year old. *I wasn't even competent enough to take care of myself.* He continued, "I would venture out into the world, get myself established and then go back to save them. That did end up happening, but not at all in the manner I planned." He stared off quietly for a few moments.

"I'll never forget the day," he said, lost in nostalgia. "I was a sophomore at OSU. It was cold and dreary outside--I was studying in my dorm room for my winter finals. I was looking forward to wrapping up the semester and going back to Wichita to spend Christmas with my family. The student dorm monitor knocked on my door and handed me a telegram. It took all of ten seconds to read, but my life was changed forever. My father had passed away of a sudden heart attack. I was needed at home right away."

I saw Mr. X's eyes start to glisten, but he regained his composure, maybe before anyone else noticed. "I talked to the dean and was granted a leave of absence to help settle my father's affairs. Knowing my modest circumstances, the dean personally paid for my bus ticket home. I've never forgotten that act of kindness when I was in need. You should find a way to have a profound impact like that for someone else at least once in your life."

"When I got home, it was even worse than I had imagined," he said. "Cootie Burger was teetering on the edge. My father had been borrowing money via business loans to keep the restaurant open and a roof barely over the family's head. I saw the look of overwhelming panic in my mother's eyes... she didn't know how to run the business. My sisters still needed providing for. I knew how important the survival of the business was to my father. One of the only emotions he clearly expressed was that Cootie Burger was his legacy. I felt I had no other options. My dreams of college and becoming an engineer died that day. I had no choice but to drop out of school, move home to take care of my family, and see if I could save our struggling family business." He was quiet for a moment. We all were.

"I wrote to the dean asking for a temporary leave. It ended up being permanent. The next time I stepped foot on campus was to receive an honorary degree decades later, not that I needed it."

"I reluctantly threw myself into my father's business, figuring out how to pay off the creditors and dig out of the hole they were living in. Things have obviously worked out, but it was a struggle. But it's the struggle that gives you inner-strength."

"So... I told you it was a long story, but that's your answer to *why hamburgers*," he said. We all shared a quiet moment. The next hour of questions were basically snoozers, but I'll give you the highlights:

How much money should you leave your kids?

"I like Warren Buffett's thoughts on this: you should leave your children enough to where they can afford to do anything. But not so much that they can afford to do nothing. You want to avoid a Vanderbilt situation where wealth ruins your offspring."

What is leadership?

"There are many definitions of leadership that are useful. Here's my version: I view it as a five-step process. Step one: see a problem for what it is. Not worse than it is; not better than it is. I often ask myself 'Why?' three or four times to help drill down to the root problem. That's what you want to address. The biggest mistake I find leaders make is not seeing for themselves. As Gorbachev supposedly told President Reagan, 'It is better to see once than to hear a hundred times.'"

"Step two: have a vision of what could be. It often helps to have a strong *why* behind what you're trying to improve. Where there's a *why*, there's a way. That motivation keeps you going when you want to quit. And I've found that just when everything looked darkest, victory and success were not far away. It just takes pushing through that last difficult patch."

"Step three: set high standards for *yourself* first. In just about every situation in life, you have to be willing to go first. Hold yourself to the highest standards."

"Step four: set high standards for others. Notice how you have to set high standards for yourself first? No one wants to follow a hypocrite. Expectations for others have to be clear and agreed upon."

"Finally, five: take action. Perfect is the enemy of good enough. Yes, it's important to make decisions supported by data, but realize you're never going to have all the numbers to feel completely confident. You still have to move forward at some point. There are very few decisions you can't undo, so just making a decision and being willing to change keeps you moving forward."

Then someone asked a good one.

What was your most difficult moment, and how did you deal with it?

"Are you sure you want to hear this one?" he asked. "OK, I will tell you this story to help you realize that life throws everyone curveballs. No one has it easy and everyone struggles."

"I mentioned before that I have… had an amazing wife. Losing her was an incredibly difficult process. I'm not sure I'll ever recover. What's made it even more difficult is the strain on the relationship with my daughter. We don't speak anymore. She told me that she never wants to see me again." The room was funeral quiet for a few moments while he composed himself. I'm ashamed to admit it, but I was imagining what dirt Mr. X's daughter would have for me if I could get her dishing on her father.

"The point is, life is full of dark moments. You can't hide from them. Let's talk about something happier now, please."

Mr. X had endured a difficult life. Fate had twisted him in complicated ways. I imagined those same forces would have broken a lesser man. I would later find out how complicated his story really was, and that he was barely scratching the surface.

CHAPTER 13

"Who's next?" asked Mr. X. Two students raised their hands, but he didn't even look in their direction. Instead, he was staring at me again. "You've been conspicuously quiet so far, Mr. Journalist. I'm curious, do you have a question for me?" His eyes bore straight into my soul. *He knows!*

I looked down at the table to avoid his piercing stare. The five seconds of silence felt like an eternity. "Actually, just one," I began. "What was the one insight you've had that created the biggest impact? Something that took twenty percent of your effort, but did eighty percent of the heavy lifting?"

"That's a surprisingly good question, young man," he said, narrowing his eyes in judgment. "Let me tell you another story from my youth. When I was in my mid-teens, my father had a friend named Eric. Eric was an interesting fellow, always into obscure hobbies. Most fascinating was Eric's obsession with falconry. Do you know what that is? He had a pet hawk that he trained for hunting. It was quite the sight to behold. A wild animal is very powerful to see in person."

I recalled myself as a kid loving the book *My Side of the Mountain*. It was about Sam Gribley, a 13-year-old boy who hated living in his parents' cramped New York City apartment with eight siblings. Sam decides to run away to an abandoned farm in the Catskill Mountains to live by himself in the wilderness. He inhabited a hollowed out tree and had a pet peregrine falcon he hunted with. As soon as I got my first pocket knife as a young boy, I was obsessed with the idea of scratching out a meager, tree-hollowed survival on my own. *Check that "meager survival" box so far as an adult...*

"Training a hawk is a big commitment," Mr. X said, interrupting my childhood daydream. "To get the most out of your bird, you have to keep it at the perfect weight. The bird has to be slightly starved before it will hunt. A fully-fed bird just sits there fat and happy. But too hungry and the bird's performance suffers from low energy. 'Hungry, but not weakened,' was how Eric described this perfect state. At that balance point, the bird has incredible clarity, energy, and singularity of purpose toward its most important objective: hunting. Eric told me that falconers have a specific term for that state. They call it *yarak*. Eric would occasionally take me out with him to see his bird hunt. There was *nothing* that would prevent that bird from tearing its prey to shreds. A bird in yarak is the purest expression of its genetic capabilities. You did not want to be a rabbit nearby when Eric's bird was in full yarak." *Where was he going with all of this?*

"Where was I going with this?" Mr. X smiled coyly. "Oh yeah, the insight. The concept of yarak doesn't apply to only falconry. Have you heard of the personal finance idea of 'Pay Yourself First?' Basically, you take money out of your account every month in an automated way to save for the future, and then you live on whatever's left. Pay yourself first before you pay everyone else. Sometimes you have to get creative to make ends meet and not dip into your savings. You create an artificial constraint, a hunger, this state of *yarak* in yourself. Yarak sparks a creativity that can only be unlocked when your back is against the wall. You become the bird that *has* to hunt."

Through a lot of nodding heads, he continued, "Yarak also applies to running a business. Most businesses hustle to create revenue, pay out their various expenses, and with any luck, there's a little profit left over for the owners. Here's what you're probably learning in business school: *Revenue minus expenses equals profits*. Sounds sensible, right?" He paused for the group of nodding heads. "Well, it's not! It is completely backwards. It should be taught: *Revenue minus PROFITS equal expenses."*

Our chaperoning professors did their best to hide their cloudy faces, but it was clear Mr. X didn't mind offending them. "Don't wait to see if there's anything left over for a profit. By carving out a margin before you address expenses, you create a constraint on the resources available. This constraint unlocks your creativity to meet customers' needs, streamline operations, and only spend money on that which truly generates value. There's no room left for fluff and bloat. Difficult decisions on how you should run your business become obvious. No longer fat, dumb and happy, maybe you make that extra sales call or hold off on that unnecessary expense. Business is very competitive, and the difference between the Hall of Fame and the graveyard can be remarkably thin. Everyone says they want to run a tight ship, but the best way to harness your entrepreneurial verve is to tie your own hands to the yarak mast. It will turn all of your business *SHOULDS* into business *MUSTS*. I've spent a lot of time finding different places to apply the idea of yarak, and it never ceases to amaze me how helpful it is. So that's my eighty-twenty secret. Shh… don't tell anyone," he whispered.

As Mr. X was finishing, his secretary appeared. "That's all the time we have for today," she said. *Damn, that went by too fast. I certainly didn't have enough material yet to write my exposé. A rebel like this must have skeletons in the closet somewhere though.* "Mr. X wanted to do one last nice thing and buy you all lunch," she said. "We've arranged to have a meal at Mr. X's favorite steakhouse. Your bus will take you there now. Unfortunately, he has an important meeting scheduled and won't be able to join you." We all clapped for Mr. X sharing his wisdom and for the free steak lunch.

Only later would I discover where Mr. X was going. And that it would eventually break my heart.

CHAPTER 14

Mr. X and his secretary conferred behind the podium while we packed up. They looked over at me and I pretended not to be staring. They went back to talking--maybe they weren't looking at me after all. Mr. X nodded and gave us a brief wave as he exited the conference room through a side door.

We made our way toward the main exit, excitedly sharing our favorite parts of the experience. Larry's eyes were wild with possibility. "That was better than advertised!" he said. "I can't wait to be as wealthy as Mr. X someday!" *I don't think that was the important takeaway, Larry.*

Meandering toward the back of the pack in my usual way, I felt a tap on my shoulder. I turned and saw Mr. X's secretary standing studiously before me. "Hi, my name is Cathy. Mr. X was impressed with your question and responses. He wants to know if you might be open to a special project?"

Jackpot! This was exactly the break I needed to dig deeper into Mr. X's operation and find out where the bodies were buried. I didn't want to appear too eager though. "Uhh… I don't know. I guess it depends on what it is? I'm pretty busy with school and work right now." *When you have the winning hand, you can afford to slow play it.*

"Well, given your background as a journalist and your interest in business, it could be right up your alley," she said. "We don't have time to discuss the details right now, but here's my card. Think about it for a few days and then let's discuss over the phone."

"Thanks, Cathy," I said. "I'll definitely think about it."

"Enjoy your lunch," she said. On the inside, I smiled like the Grinch about to wreck Christmas. *This was all shaping up nicely.*

CHAPTER 15

"What was that all about?" Larry asked as I caught up with him at the elevator.

"Oh, nothing. She just asked a question--not important." *What Larry doesn't know won't hurt him.* "Let's feast!" I said, knowing it would throw him off my tracks.

We enjoyed a fantastic steak lunch, courtesy of Mr. X. The restaurant was a dimly lit, wood-paneled affair that was charming enough and served large slabs of Kansas beef. I'm not sure what our vegan classmate ate--green beans and a baked potato?

To curry favor with Mr. X and increase the odds of future students being invited back, the group spent the rest of the afternoon volunteering at the Wichita YMCA in Mr. X's name, each of us given different menial chores. Some were assigned to cleaning. Others organized sporting equipment and books. Larry and I *(mostly Larry)* must have looked somewhat handy as we were charged with putting together a bookshelf using a thrift store toolbox. *Who needs Bob Vila?*

Finishing up our good deeds at the YMCA, we were turned loose for dinner. Larry and I dragged the other students back to last night's BBQ joint. It didn't disappoint for a second round. The beer continued to flow and the hours slipped by. Before we knew it, it was late, and we all had early flights westward.

I needed a few aspirin in the morning to nurse my hangover. I spent most of the flight home examining Cathy's card while game-planning how I might use Mr. X's special project to my advantage. It could be any number of things; I simply didn't know. I also didn't know I was actually the one being played.

CHAPTER 16

Back to the grind. A daunting school load and an endless stream of deliverables at Big Rock threatened to sink me in my first week back. One evening that week, as I walked home after a particularly mind-numbing day at the office, I got a call from my parents. *Strange, why were they both on the line?*

"Nick, your mother and I have something important to tell you."

"You're having another baby? I'm going to be a big brother again--that's great!"

"What… no," my dad said. "Nick, this is serious."

"Sorry, what is it?"

My mom started with an odd tone, "Well, as you know, we've never been the best with money. We've always worked for something more important than money. We haven't been very good about saving. It always felt like we could just make more."

Dad's turn, "We took some money out of our home equity when the prices were high. I made some investments in green energy… they didn't work out. Long story short, the home prices aren't as high now and my billings are down, so there's less money coming in."

Mom cut in suddenly sobbing, "We could lose the house, Nicky!"

"Don't cry, dear," my dad consoled in the background. "We just need to borrow a little money to get by until work picks back up. We figured since you have that fancy job at Big Stone..."

"Big Rock, Dad," I said. *If you're going to ask for money, at least get the name right.*

"Oh, Big Rock. Anyway, do you think you can help, son?" he asked. "It's only temporary. We'll pay you back in no time. Please, we don't want to lose the house."

Not that many months ago I had been worrying about myself having to live under an overpass. It was still a distinct possibility if the whole Big Rock thing didn't work out. Turns out it might be a family reunion. It now made sense why they'd been weirdly relieved to hear about my corporate job.

"Honestly, I don't have very much saved, but I'll send what I can," I said.

"Thank you, son," they both said with genuine relief.

I hung up and just stared off vacantly. *My god, how do I avoid becoming like my parents? Years of work and nothing to show for it.*

Then it all clicked. I could kill two birds with one stone. I pulled out Cathy's business card, the edges warn from my scheming fingers. I dialed her number.

"Hello? This is Cathy speaking."

"Hi, Cathy. This is Nick, the student you offered the special project to."

"Oh yes," she said. "How are you? I was hoping you'd call."

"I'm good, thanks. Are you still looking for help?"

"Yes, we are."

"Great," I said. "I'd love to hear more about the project."

"Here's what we had in mind. You'd fly out to Wichita every few weeks to spend the day interviewing Mr. X. He'd like you to write an in-depth profile. But that piece is really an audition for a bigger job: writing a full biography for Mr. X. There have been a few written already, but this would be the first authorized one with direct access. Mr. X can be reclusive, but he wants a book that finally tells his story and shares his business knowledge. He'd pay for the travel and offer a stipend for your time. I can handle all of the travel logistics for you." *Bingo, a stipend.* I can gain access to the inner-sanctum of capitalism while also scraping some extra bread together to help my parents financially. *I love it when a plan comes together.*

"That sounds like quite the project. I'm honored you want my help," I said. "I'd have to get it cleared with school and work before I could say yes. But I'm definitely interested."

"OK, why don't you find out in the next day or two and let me know?" Cathy said.

"Will do."

Then she said something that gave me chills. "Can you keep a secret?"

"Yes," I said. *Probably truthfully.*

"Mr. X isn't in the best of health. He couldn't join you guys for lunch last week because he was undergoing serious medical tests. We honestly don't know how much time he has left, so we'd want to get started right away. And we'd appreciate your discretion."

"Of course," I said. "I'll call you tomorrow with a firm yes or no."

"Thanks, Nick."

I called my academic advisor and relayed the opportunity. She was very encouraging and we worked out an independent study course which allowed me to get school credit for the project. *Sweet, everything is coming up roses!* I think the school was rubbing their hands together with the potential windfall of a big donation down the line. *I wasn't going to tell them that you don't become a billionaire by giving it all away.*

What about Big Rock? That was a cinch. They were an automatic yes and always ready to add a deep-pocketed client. What better way to land a Wichita billionaire than having an inside man? They also promised to shift some of my project responsibilities around to free up my time. That never happened in practice, but it was a nice idea in theory. Projects and deadlines still rained down on me with a torrid pace.

I called Cathy and informed her that I was in. She said she'd make the arrangements. *I hope you have an iron butt, I said to myself, because you're going to spending a lot of time wedged into an airplane seat.*

CHAPTER 17

Around the time I was hired by Big Rock, I met a girl. (*Yes, this is that kind of story--don't roll your eyes.*) She was a barista in a local coffee shop I frequented. According to the pin on her apron, her name was Stephanie. We flirted in three minute transactions for a few months. In that time, I figured out she poured coffee in the morning for extra spending money, but was really in a Ph.D. program at the local university. Her area of research was psychology, specifically decision-making. I didn't understand half of the terms she used, but I nodded enthusiastically like I did. *You're right, I was doing a lot of nodding and pretending these days.* She was the smartest girl I had ever been interested in, and being a sucker for girls in ball caps, I was smitten.

It took all of those months to work up the courage to ask her out. I imagined she was hit on more than a boxer's speed bag at both school and work, so I expected her to say no. At least she'd know how to let me down easy with all the practice. Plus, there were plenty of other coffee shops I could go to after I'd sullied this one with unrequited love.

To my surprise she said yes, and we picked an evening later in the week to grab a beer. *A coffee date seemed too on the nose.*

Date night rolled around and I was nervous as all hell. Yet after a brief period of awkward small talk, we really started connecting. I loved hearing about her psychology research and she didn't seem to mind when I talked about what I did at work and school. It was the first time I'd felt this kind of chemistry--an electric intoxication. Toward the end of the date, there was a lull in the conversation and a clear eye-contact invitation... I couldn't help myself from kissing her. *Just kidding, you should know me better by now: I totally chickened out.* Instead, we agreed to another date to see if the chemistry wasn't a fluke.

Our next date had more great conversation. This time when the conversation lull occurred, she saved us both and kissed me before I could screw it up. Several more dinners ensued, our conversations getting deeper. I let my guard down. I started hearing cheesy love songs on the radio... and they were making sense! *WTF?!* This must have been what they were talking about. My previous interactions with the fairer sex felt acting out a confused cultural dance. Steph and I were just easy and natural.

After several more dates, I took her on my favorite mountain hike. We rock-hopped up a quiet stream that meandered its way through large granite boulders. The payoff is thirty-feet of waterfall grandeur. It was a beautiful hidden gem of a hike. There was a secluded grove of trees close by where you could still hear the waterfall purring in the distance. We made love for the first time on a blanket in that grove. The diffused light in the trees made for an ethereal experience.

We were in love and all was right in the world. *For the time being at least.*

CHAPTER 18

My first Wichita trip--I was stoked! A few days before my departure, I received a cryptic note from Mr. X in the mail. It had a printed quote with his hand-scribbled addendum:

> *Every day, in countless ways, the competitive position of each of our businesses grows either weaker or stronger. If we are delighting customers, eliminating unnecessary costs and improving our products and services, we gain strength. But if we treat customers with indifference or tolerate bloat, our businesses will wither. On a daily basis, the effects of our actions are imperceptible; cumulatively, though, their consequences are enormous. When our long-term competitive position improves as a result of these almost unnoticeable actions, we describe the phenomenon as "widening the moat."*
>
> *-- Warren Buffett*

> *Think about this quote on the flight out. See you in a few days.*
>
> *- Mr. X*

I didn't know what to think and just prayed there wouldn't be a pop quiz. Upon landing, I made my way through the now familiar Wichita Dwight D. Eisenhower National Airport. Cathy was waiting for me as I exited the baggage area.

"Welcome back to Wichita, Nick," she said smiling, her arms opening. "Just so you know, we're big on hugs here. Well, Mr. X isn't, but I am!" Caught off guard but not wanting to offend, I offered up a one-armed, side lean-in job. She smoothly pivoted me like her last name was Gracie and I found myself on the receiving end of one of the strongest, most authentic hugs of my life. Something inside me thawed and I found myself liking Cathy noticeably more than ten seconds earlier. *Huh, maybe these cheerful Midwesterns were onto something?* In today's world of social media posturing, it's hard to disrupt the feeling of a genuine hug.

"Thank you, it's good to be back, Cathy."

"By the way, we're not going to the office. Mr. X has something… *different* in mind. You'll be joining him for one of his favorite activities." My mind immediately jumped to golfing, yachting, or maybe swimming in a giant bin of gold coins. *Isn't that what billionaires did for fun?*

"And I hope you don't mind getting a little greasy," she said with a knowing smile. I played along, raising my eyebrows.

We walked to her nondescript American-made car and made our way through town. After several turns I was completely ensconced in my own little world. I was staring out the window at passersby, trying to imagine what it was like for them to wake up in Wichita every day. I remembered one of mom's hippy friends once relaying the advice of a zen master: every stranger you see, in your head wish them happiness. Nothing more or less. *I wish you happiness, frazzled-looking soccer mom yelling at her kids in the backseat. Nothing more or less.*

We eventually pulled into the parking lot of a Cootie Burger. It was early in the afternoon. The lunch rush should have been over, but the restaurant was still hopping. There was a flurry of activity behind the counter. Young people in starched white attire and red aprons were preparing hamburgers and pressing raw potatoes into slivers of fries. If you didn't know better, they looked like they were dancing with each other in their efficiency. Their music, the whir of the milkshake machine. In the customer seating area, I saw Mr. X dressed in a pair of chinos and a Cootie Burger polo. He was smiling while talking to a young family.

"This is one of our flagship stores," Cathy said. "We use this to test different initiatives and ideas. Mr. X loves to come down here to see the latest developments."

Finishing up his conversation, Mr. X made his way over to us and greeted me with a smile. "Hello, it's nice to see you again, Nick. I hope you had a pleasant flight?"

"Not too bad," I said. "I got a lot of work done."

"That's great. Welcome to what I call 'The Lab,'" he said with a dramatic sweep of his hand. He was a bit of showman. Cathy had clearly heard this before as she wandered off to chit-chat with the store manager.

"Cathy was just telling me this is where you test new ideas," I started. "I have to be honest, it looks like every other fast food place I've been in. I don't see a lot of testing going on?"

"I'll admit it's subtle," he said. "We can't be too radical with any changes, especially if they go against our brand. A brand is like a promise of a specific experience. If we were to make big changes, it'd be confusing for our customers. You can't come in for a hamburger and find only tacos on the menu."

"That makes sense, I guess," I said.

"I'm glad you accepted the offer, Nick," Mr. X said. "Here's how I want things to go: for the first few sessions, I'll be covering some business basics with you. I want us to be speaking a common language. Then we can worry about the less interesting stuff like my life story. I usually prefer to ask more questions than give answers. But in this case, I imagine I'll be doing a lot of the talking. Please, jump in with your own questions though. I want to make sure you understand the concepts. Is this an acceptable arrangement for you?"

"Yes, sir." *Perfect, the more he talks, the more rope he lets out to eventually hang himself.*

"Good, because I'm old and rich and used to getting my way," he said with a wry smile.

"I bet you are," I said.

"Let's dive right in," he said cheerfully. "It's been my observation that many in business are looking for a silver bullet. Something you fire once and it's game over. It's human nature to look for these shortcuts. My view is that there are no silver bullets. You're either getting slightly better or worse every single day. There's no stasis, and one percent change is barely noticeable in isolation. Did you read the note I sent?"

"I did," I said. "I guess I didn't quite understand."

"Here's a little quiz," he said. *Damn it.* "If you could get one percent better at something every day, how much would you improve in one year?"

I knew this was a trick question and you couldn't just add up one percent 365 times. "It's more than 365% because of compounding, so like five times better?" I said.

"You're right about the compounding," he said. "But you're not even close on the effect. The answer is thirty-seven times better by the end of one year. I know people your age are dependent upon calculators," he said with a teasing wink. "All you have to do is plug in one-point-oh-one to the power of three-sixty-five. Here's another quiz: if you got one percent worse every day, how much would you deteriorate?"

My first thought was -365%, but that made no sense so I simply guessed, "Umm, eighty percent worse?"

"I guess math isn't your strong suit," he said teasingly. "The answer is minus ninety-seven percent. Point-nine-nine to the power of three-sixty-five on your calculator."

"Wow, so one percent better is a thirty-seven x and one percent worse knocks you down to three percent? That's a big difference," I said.

"Humans evolved in a linear environment, so we're not wired to appreciate the power of compounding. In this lab, we're looking for tiny one percent improvements that will echo throughout the rest of our restaurant system. Progress that is barely noticeable here starts to really add real value over millions of burgers, fries, shakes, and customer interactions."

"How do you know if what you're testing is adding more value?" I wondered aloud.

"That's a very astute question," he said. "I'm impressed. It starts with being thoughtful at every level of the company," he said. "Every year, we sit down to do the company budget. At most organizations, they start with what they did last year and make a few simple adjustments. One study found that one-third of all companies change their budgets by one percent or less from year-to-year. How slow are you to change if only one percent of your resources are changing?"

"Glacial," I said.

"We practice something called *zero-based budgeting*," he said. "Basically, every expense needs to be justified each year. Nothing just rolls over mindlessly without passing inspection. What do you think is the primary filter that we use to evaluate these expenses?"

"Is it something like ten percent less than what competitors spend? That way you're guaranteed to be more efficient," I said. *I'll admit I was feeling a little proud of myself for such a logical answer.*

"Not a bad guess, but you're wrong," Mr. X said. *Swing and a miss.* "Here's the filter we use: *Will this expense go toward delighting our customer?* If the answer is no, then we're ruthless about cutting it. We call these *non-strategic* expenses because they don't advance our strategy of making the customer happy. We've found these expenses to be like fingernails; they always need trimming."

I chuckled at his joke, but added, "Isn't that close to what I said with spending less than your competitors?"

"Sort of, but here's the catch," he said. "We also have something we call *strategic* expenses. These expenses advance our strategy of delighting the customer. For strategic expenses, we seek to *outspend* the competition by a long shot. Strategic expenses build a moat around our castle so the customer only wants to do business with us. We aren't afraid to spend in those categories. We view them as investing in the happiness of our customers."

"So you only spend money if you think it will benefit the customer?" I asked.

"Yes," he said. "We try to focus on things that are unlikely to change. Will customers ever want a less clean restaurant? Will they ever want longer wait times? Will they ever want lower quality ingredients? Probably not."

"I think that Buffett quote you sent me makes a little sense now," I said. "All that jazz about delighting customers and removing unnecessary expenses."

"That's right. An example might help. There are a couple of stories which have become Cootie Burger folklore. When I bought one of the first buildings when we were expanding, it was in really shabby shape. I knew it needed at least a fresh coat of paint if we were to have any customers. After all, who wants to eat in a dilapidated dump?"

"Not me," I said.

"The building backed up to another complex so there were really only three sides of the structure that anyone would ever see. Being frugal, I only painted the three exposed sides, cutting my paint budget by twenty-five percent. There's now a running joke in the company where people will tease each other by saying, '*You're trying to paint the fourth wall!*' The implication being what they're advocating is a non-strategic expense. 'Not painting the fourth wall' is now ingrained in our culture."

"I see," I said. The light bulb was starting to brighten. "What was the other story?"

"Have you ever heard of pink slime?" he asked. "There were some news reports about it a few years back."

"Sounds vaguely familiar. Was that some gross cow leftovers?"

"Close, the technical name was 'lean finely textured beef.' It was added to a lot of hamburger meat as a filler. Seventy percent of ground beef sold in US supermarkets contained it. As you can imagine, it was a way to lower expenses. And beef is one of your bigger costs for a hamburger restaurant. We had the option of doing what everyone else was doing to reduce costs and used beef that had pink slime. But at Cootie Burger, we believed that higher quality beef was noticeably better and made a difference for our customers, so we proudly outspent the competition. Higher quality beef was a *strategic* expense. When the pink slime news story went mainstream, many competitors saw their sales drop. We, however, experienced an upswing in sales—building our moat, to use Mr. Buffett's term."

"I bet you felt vindicated," I said. "Let me ask a foolish question."

"Are you capable of any other kind?" he said jocularly. "And by the way, feel free to order yourself something to eat," he said, motioning toward the counter. "I'm buying." *At least this job came with some fringe-fry benefits. OK, that was bad. I'll show myself out.*

I was enjoying my education, but school was about to *really* be in session.

CHAPTER 19

I went to the counter and ordered myself a Cootie burger with the fried egg on top, fries and a large shake. *No sense holding back if he's buying, right?* As I rejoined Mr. X, I fired him a question: "You could probably sell all of the hamburgers you wanted if each one came with say, a free trip to Hawaii. That's an exaggeration, but how do you know when you're spending too much, even if it seems strategic? A trip to Hawaii would certainly delight them."

"That's not a foolish question," he replied. "Sit down here and I'll show you something important." With that, he shuffled off behind the restaurant counter.

I sat at one of the open booths, excited to enjoy a famous Cootie burger. I expected Mr. X to take the vacant side of the booth, as was customary in Western culture. But when he returned, he stood waiting expectantly on my side until I got the hint and slid in. He sat down next to me with a handful of straws, a pencil, and a piece of paper. He proceeded to arrange the straws into rudimentary triangles and made some scribbles on the paper.

"This is the Iron Law of Economic Survival," he began.

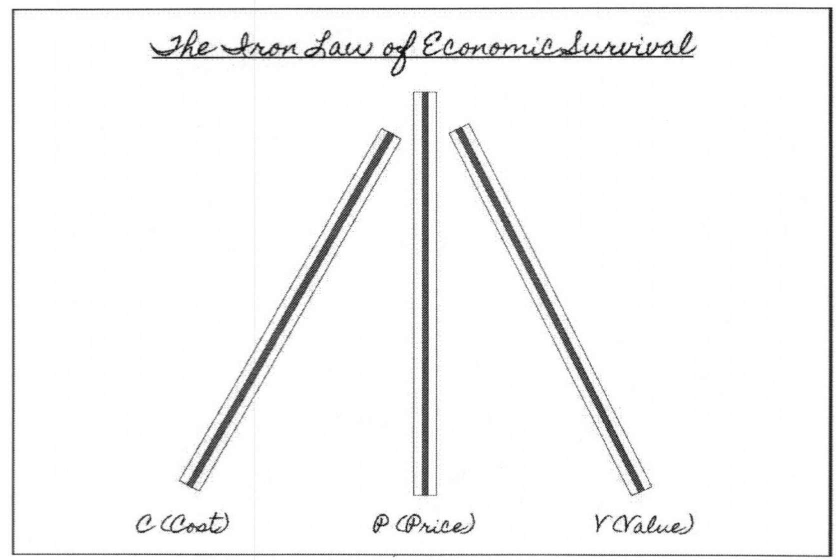

"Commit this to memory," he said with a serious tone. "In order for a business to thrive, the value delivered to the customer, *V*, has to be greater than the price the customer is charged, *P*, which has to be greater than the cost of that good or service, *C*. *V* is greater than *P* is greater than *C*," he said, pointing to each. "They can be in a different order for brief periods of time, but anything other than *C* then *P* then *V* is not sustainable. Either the customer will stop buying, your business will go bankrupt, or both."

"I'm with you, keep going," I said.

"OK, let's address each letter individually. First *C*. What does *cost* actually mean here?" he asked.

I thought for a moment and then answered, "In general, businesses have costs to make stuff. They have to pay for employees, buy equipment, buildings, inventory, advertising, lobby politicians to look the other way. Is that what you mean?" *I couldn't help myself from sneaking in a little jab.*

"That's an OK start," he said, his frown likely a response to my social commentary. "The correct answer is really 'all of the above.' Every cost should be included in that *C* number. The more comprehensive your list, the better your calculation of true economic cost. It's very easy to use accounting tricks to make *C* be whatever you want by shifting costs into different time periods. Always be wary and ask yourself does this represent every true cost? Don't fool yourself. And don't let others fool you with their projections. Let's see if you can do better with *P*?" he said, pointing to the middle straw.

"This seems straightforward," I hazaraded. "It's the price you receive for selling something?"

"Alright, that one was kind of easy," he said. "Let me add some nuance. It's helpful to look at the price through different time periods. For instance, what if you sold something like a newspaper subscription where the customer kept paying every month. That first month's price, one transaction, wouldn't tell the whole story. Often it is better to look at the customer's lifetime relationship to determine accurate costs and prices."

"Here's something I've always wondered," I said. "How do you know what price you can charge?" *I wanted to test his thoughts on price-gouging.*

"That sounds like a very simple question, but the answer is anything but. We can talk about it later. That simple question takes us down all kinds of rabbit holes. Competition, game theory, psychology. Let's put a pin in that for now, but I will give you a general rule of thumb: if you have more than five competitors in your fishbowl, don't expect to be able to control the price of anything. Also, I've noticed that in the long run, a mature market becomes a two-horse race. Usually an old, reliable brand versus an upstart battling it out. Think Coke and Pepsi locking horns in the Cola Wars."

"Fair enough," I said. *I could snare him on that subject later.*

"How about the toughest one, *V*?" Mr. X said. "I'll have to warn you, centuries of philosophers have worked on what makes something valuable."

That's not very encouraging. As I started to feel the tickle of panic, my food arrived. I looked at Mr. X and he nodded to say go ahead and dig in. So I did. I could feel him observing me as I took the first few bites, like he was measuring my enjoyment. *Maybe he was sliding straws around in his head?*

Mr. X's warning made me doubt that I could come up with a good answer. My mind wandered back to my comically-sparse apartment for clues while I ate. I did have a relatively nice hand-me-down coffee table. *A dim flash of possible insight sputtered in my mind.* "It seems like the more effort someone had to put into something, the more valuable it must be. For instance, I'd expect to get more value out of a coffee table that was handcrafted than some piece of junk slapped together. Wouldn't it be better and deliver more value? So maybe one measurement of value is stored up human time or effort?"

"You don't know it, but you're in very good company with that guess. Ever heard of Adam Smith?" he asked.

"Wasn't he the lead singer of some British band in the '80s? The Smiths, right?" *He didn't seem to get my joke.*

"No, the Adam Smith I'm referring to was an economist in the 1700s. He shared your thought: that value comes from the amount of labor needed to create something. A more complete theory eventually came along though. It's called the 'theory of subjective value.' Sounds confusing, but it's pretty simple when you hear it. We all have wants and needs at different times. They vary with the condition you're experiencing. If you're drowning in a river, a glass of water isn't of much use. If you're stranded in the desert, it's almost infinitely valuable to you. The value of something always depends on your individual context."

"Oh, like you only really want an umbrella when it's raining, otherwise it's a pain to carry around?" I said.

"Right, every human has a list buried in their head that's the order of their wants and needs at that given moment. Entrepreneurs work hard to identify and satisfy items on that list. The list usually changes slowly. You regularly need food, water, shelter, clothing. But there are occasional massive upheavals to our lists. For five thousand years, everyone wanted a better horse saddle. Then one day, the automobile turned over the subjective apple cart. Now people weren't so interested in saddles. They needed gas, oil, and tires."

"Or a smart-phone?" I said, imagining it might be a big change in technology. "Now people need apps and data like they need oxygen."

"I'll have to take your word for it," he said. *Old people.* "Remember, each person's list is their own, and it's completely subjective to their experience. The best steak in the world may be repulsive to your vegan classmate. Some people would feel guilty driving an expensive, ostentatious car. Your list is uniquely your own and changes based on your environment and the options available."

"I see," I said. "I guess my coffee table is valuable because it can hold my drink upright, not because it took someone a lot of effort to create it."

"That's right. There are startling implications in understanding the subjective theory of value," he said. "Let me give you another concrete example."

"Shoot," I said.

"There was a plan to spend six *billion* dollars to redo the railway track from London to Paris," he said. "Engineers believed this would improve the passenger experience by cutting thirty minutes off a four-hour journey. Less time on the train is a good thing, right? But what if instead they spent only six *million* dollars to add TV sets into every seat and also provided passengers with free movies? Couldn't they spend 1/1000th of the original price and make the ride feel even shorter than the thirty minute proposed reduction?" I nodded in thought. "They didn't think very hard about what would make the customer more happy. The obvious engineering answer isn't always right due to the subjective nature of experience."

"Time flies when you're having fun," I joked. "Maybe they'd even want to sit at the station and finish their movie, making the trip a little longer?"

"Probably not," he said, derailing me. "All of this is just a long way of saying perceived value is based on what the individual consumer feels and experiences. Look at that counter over there." The employees were still hustling with smiles on their faces. "Every employee at Cootie Burger is empowered to spend up to twenty dollars, with no questions asked, to make a customer happy. Why do we do that?"

"I think I might know," I said. "The people closest to the customer probably have the best gauge on how to fix a problem or what might delight the customer. If you're at headquarters a thousand miles away and are making decisions in a vacuum away from your customers, how do you know if you are hitting the mark? How can you tell what is a *strategic* versus a *non-strategic* expense? You can't--there's no feedback when you're so far away."

He smiled when I used his terminology. I felt the ache of internal conflict, at the edge of my subconscious. Some part of me was eager for Mr. X's approval. Why should I care? "That's exactly right, Nick," he said. "That's why I come down to the Lab on a regular basis. I don't want to get too far from our customers. It's also why we push a healthy portion of our decision-making out to the frontlines and give employees the latitude of twenty dollars no-questions-asked. We feel it gives us a chance to increase our V as much as possible for every unit of C. Do you know anything about World War II?"

"A little," I said.

"Well, I lived through it," he said. "The Nazis were on a horrifying mission, but the German army did some really smart things in an organizational sense. They had this concept called *auftragstaktik*."

"Off-rag-stak-what?" I said. *That was more of a mouthful than my Cootie burger.*

"Don't worry about the name," he said. "Focus on the concept. The Nazi upper command would tell their soldiers *what* they wanted accomplished and *why* it was important. It was then up to the lower ranks in the field to come up with *how* it gone done. They get bigger picture strategy from above, but operational flexibility in the field where the environment is dynamic and messy. The pieces on the commander's mapboard don't always fit with what's happening in the field. They wanted the German soldiers to feel empowered to make decisions and be creative in achieving their directives. The Germans were often outnumbered, but they were one of the most effective armies ever assembled. A lot of that was due to their thoughtful decision-making structure. Just because their aims were so awful doesn't mean we can't learn something useful from them."

I imagined myself on the front lines driving a tank, the engine shuddering while a German commander shouted orders at me. "So you want your soldiers to feel empowered to make decisions as well?"

"Yes, you're starting to pick it up," he said. He glanced at his watch. "That's all I have time for today. When you finish your meal, Cathy will take you to the airport. Spend some time thinking about your CPV triangles. See you in a few weeks."

Before I could I say anything, he had shuffled out the door. *I flew all this way for a burger and a World War II story? This might be a little harder than I thought.*

CHAPTER 20

My relationship with Stephanie was in full bloom. Every minute I wasn't at work, school, or on an airplane, I spent with her. I met all of her grad school friends. We'd go out in a big group for dinner together on Friday nights. Sometimes we'd go bowling after. Other times it'd be darts and shuffleboard at our favorite bar. If we drank too much, we'd usually end up dancing somewhere. Then the search was on for a 2:00 AM slice of pizza. It was a rowdy bunch, considering they were all hardworking Ph.D. students. We had a lot of fun together.

We went on regular double dates with Larry and his fiancee, Maggie. While Larry was a human mountain, Maggie was petite. The juxtaposition of the two of them was always good for a laugh. *The sheer physics of... nevermind.* They would argue with an intensity I'd only seen in romantic comedies. Yet they'd seem to come back stronger after a big blowup. Like how a bone is supposedly stronger in a place where it's broken and mended.

Stephanie and I would go on hikes when we could break away to nature. We had our best conversations walking side-by-side on a trail. There was something magical about being in nature. We drove to the closest national park for a weekend getaway. I was under a lot of stress at work and school. I needed the recharge time with someone who understood me. It gave me the strength to put on my mask and head back into the lion's den every Monday morning.

CHAPTER 21

I received a note with another Warren Buffett quote from Mr. X before my next trip:

> *"The dynamics of capitalism guarantee that competitors will repeatedly assault any business 'castle' that is earning high returns. Therefore a formidable barrier such as a company's being the low-cost producer (GEICO, Costco) or possessing a powerful world-wide brand (Coca-Cola, Gillette, American Express) is essential for sustained success."*

I have a special treat for you this week. It'll be a real shocker!
- Mr. X

I didn't know what to make of the quote, but I was looking forward to finding out what my treat might be. *When you have a billion dollars at your disposal, anything is possible, right?*

When I landed at the Wichita airport, Cathy picked me up and drove me downtown. Just before she kicked me out of the car, she told me that Mr. X was a perennial season ticket holder for the Wichita State Shockers basketball program. She said he had great seats as she handed me a ticket. I was to meet Mr. X at the game for this week's session. Oh, so that was my "shocking" treat. *All that money and only a ticket to a lousy college basketball game?* I guess it could be fun.

I entered the arena and navigated my way down near the floor where our seats were. I found Mr. X in head-to-toe black and yellow Shockers gear, ready to cheer on his team. He looked like he had been plucked from the student section and left in the sun to wither into a human raisin in all his swag. All that was missing was the face paint.

"Hi, Mr. X," I greeted him.

"Hey, Nick," he said with a genuine smile. "Have a seat."

I settled in next to him. "Great seats--we're almost close enough to get sweat on us," I said.

"I don't splurge on a lot of things relative to my wealth, but this is one of them. I love college basketball, especially Wichita State," he said. *This is splurging?* "These kids are playing for the love the game, not million dollar paydays. I respect how they leave it all out on the court."

With my upbringing, I didn't get much exposure to sports. I wasn't exactly in my element, but I did enjoy the energy of the crowd in a rocking stadium.

"I want to pick up where we left off last time," he started. "Do you remember the Iron Law of Economic Survival?"

"Yes, I made different cost-price-value triangles all week, experimenting with what you said." I wanted Mr. X to find me an apt pupil to get him to let down his guard.

"Good, maybe we won't have to go so slowly this time," he said. *That didn't feel slow to me, but whatever.*

"Let's start with a few fringe cases," Mr. X said. He broke out a clipboard and placed it on the armrests between us to fashion a small table. He pulled out a fresh sheet of paper and several Cootie Burger straws. *Who carries this kind of stuff around with them?* He started marking up the paper. The players were warming up and doing their pre-game rituals not far from our makeshift classroom. The crowd was still filing in and it was quiet enough for us to talk.

"What happens if the price straw is on the other side of the value straw?" Mr. X inquired.

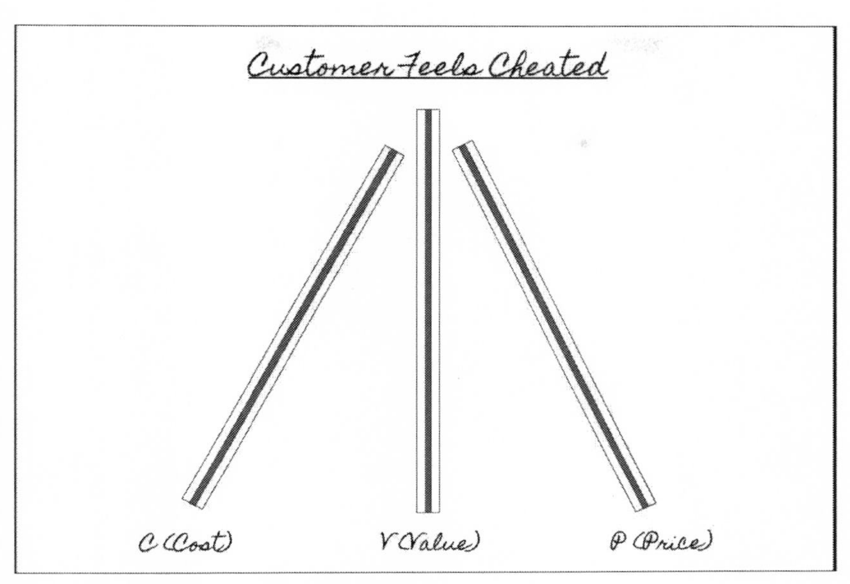

Class was in session.

This seemed pretty straightforward to me, like I might be missing something. "The customer won't think they're getting their money's worth if the price they pay is more than the value they receive. They won't end up buying. At least not for long--it's unsustainable."

"Correct," he said. "It's an opportunity for other businesses to come steal that unhappy customer. Eventually that person will find a way to stop paying for that product or service. Being cheated doesn't sit well with us for long."

"Even if it means overthrowing a totalitarian regime," I said. *Yikes, I sounded like my father. Better dial that back a bit if I want to win Mr. X's approval.*

"Or changing their laundry detergent," Mr. X said. "Here's a slightly tougher one. What if the cost straw is farther out than both the price and value straws?"

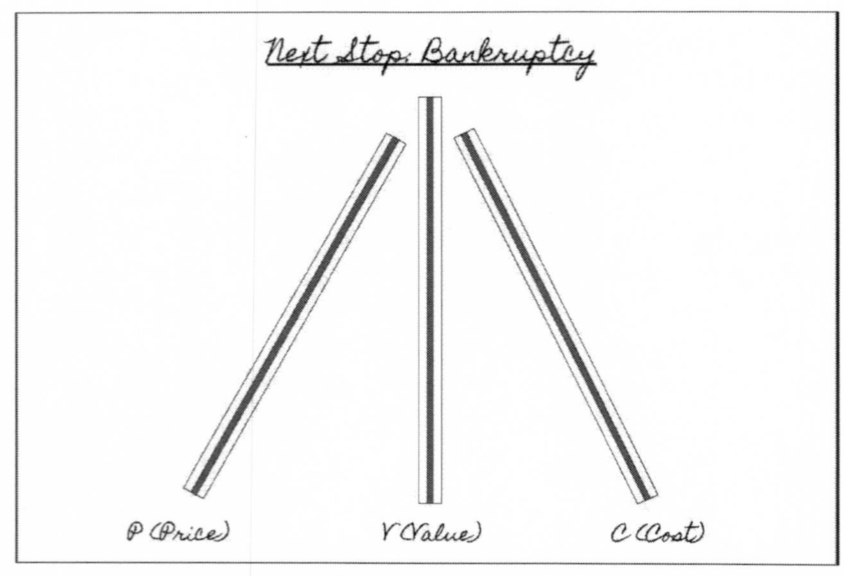

After a minute of reflection, I said, "Well, the customer feels like they're getting their money's worth, so they're happy. But as the producer, you have a problem. You're subsidizing the happiness of your customers at your own expense. Which you can only afford to do for so long before you run out of money."

"That's right," he said. "It's one of the underappreciated benefits of capitalism. Entrepreneurs end up giving away too much of the farm, to society's benefit for periods of time." It had never occurred to me that capitalism sometimes makes errors in that direction. I'd always assumed the little guy was cheated and systematically milked. *Hmmm.*

The game tipped off, the crowd roaring as the Shockers started with the ball. The teams went back and forth with intensity, but neither side getting much of advantage. Like two boxers feeling each other out in the early rounds. Eventually, there was a TV timeout. The crowd quieted down to conserve for later.

"Alright, time for our next insight," Mr. X said, taking advantage of the lull. "What would you call the wedge between *Cost* and *Price*?"

"I assume price is the money coming into the business, which is revenue…" I said, happy to be able to use some of my B-school jargon. Mr. X nodded, so I continued, "And cost is expenses, so revenue minus expense is profit." *At least those were the terms I'd memorized.*

"That's correct, that triangle represents your profit," he said, writing the word in that space.

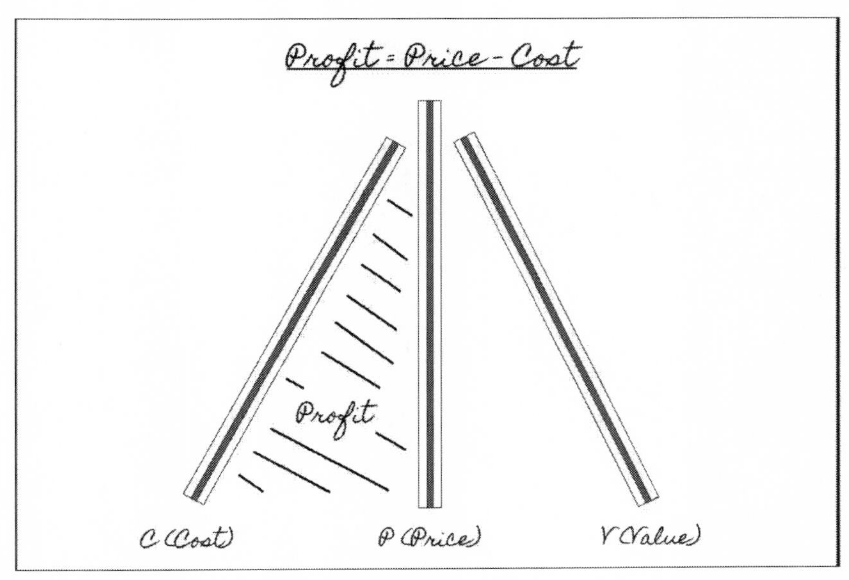

"Every company has to eventually make a profit to stay in business," he continued. "I'll have a lot more to say about profit later. I've found that many captains of industry don't fully understand its significance. This next one's a little tougher. What's the wedge formed between *Price* and *Value*?"

I smiled. We had recently covered something like this at school. "I think that would be called *consumer surplus*.

Basically, it's what the customer would have been willing to pay, but didn't have to."

"Technically speaking, you're right," he said. "But let's avoid academic jargon." *Dang.* "I like to think of that wedge as your *brand*." He wrote the word in that triangle as he said, "That extra bit of surprise value that the customer feels they got compared to the price they paid. Think of it this way: there's a piggybank in your customers' minds. With every interaction, you're either making a deposit or taking a withdrawal. The contents of the piggybank is a measurement of your brand. It exists as an abstraction scattered throughout your customers' minds, so it's all but impossible to measure. But that doesn't mean it isn't hugely important."

Bringing It All Together

Profit

Brand

C (Cost)

P (Price)

V (Value)

After the timeout, the Shockers went cold, missing several open shots. The visitors took advantage and sprinted out to a sizeable lead. Mr. X told me that it was still early and he wasn't worried. The Shockers' coach signaled angrily for a timeout to refocus the team.

"In general," Mr. X continued, "there are three ways to make the brand triangle bigger. Be the cheapest. Be the most convenient. Or be the best. Good companies aim for at least one of those objectives. Great companies find a way to achieve two. Doing all three is a rarity."

I started going through a list of companies in my head and sure enough, they were at least one of those three. "Why am I not learning this in business school?!" I wondered out loud.

Mr. X just smiled knowingly. "So now we've got value, price, and cost. We have how they interact to create profit and brand," he said, pointing to each. "This may surprise you, but we can describe an incredible variety of business situations by sliding these straws around. For instance, what if you're in the steel industry and the product you sell is a commodity? Meaning the steel you make is identical to the steel everyone else makes. How would you move the straws?"

I thought quietly for a while before responding. Mr. X was happy to watch the game while I sat in contemplation. When it quieted down between plays, I said, "Well, I assume you wouldn't have any control over the price. It will be whatever the world market price is for steel. I'd also imagine that the perceived value delivered isn't too far above that price. Unless you could offer something special like just the right quantity or shape the customer wanted. You can't be 'the best' when all the steel is the same, but maybe you could be the most convenient? Better financing terms, delivery, or billing options? I don't know. Something to make the experience a little more enjoyable or easy. But you're pretty limited on what you can do to bump up the value versus competitors. I'm sure they're quick to copy you."

"I'd agree," Mr. X said. Although his eyes were still on the action, it sent my ego ticking up a notch to have him agree. He eventually looked back at me. "This situation describes more businesses than many CEOs care to admit. More businesses are providing a commodity than they realize. There's a saying: *In the long run, everything is a toaster.* Meaning, it's very hard to create and maintain a differentiated product for a long time. There's simply too much competition vying to scratch our subjective human itches. It's just a matter of time before you get disrupted."

"You said many don't realize they're in a commodity business," I said. "How would you know if you're providing a differentiated product then?"

"The answer is surprisingly simple. You only have to answer *yes* to one question: *If you wanted to, could you raise prices and not lose customers?* If you can answer *yes*, you probably have a differentiated product. If the answer is *no*, you're in a commodity business. It's that simple. There's nothing wrong with providing a commodity, by the way. You're often keeping the wheels of the world turning. But it does change what you should focus on. Care to take a guess what I'm hinting at? It's staring you plain in the face."

I honed in on the straws, willing them to whisper to me an answer. There was only one lever we hadn't addressed, so I ventured, "It must have something to do with cost since we haven't moved that straw in a while."

"You might be onto something...," Mr. X said leadingly. We sat for a moment as I mulled it over. *How can he be so close to Death's door, and yet so damned patient?*

"So are you saying that if you can't raise the price, you should focus primarily on controlling costs?" I asked.

"That's exactly what I'm saying," he replied. "There are many commodity businesses that make a great profit because they are the lowest cost provider in their industry. They know they can't do much to change value and price, so they become demons on lowering costs. It's important to be strategic about where you are pressing your advantage. Take the Shockers--they have a great offense. They space the floor well, move without the ball, and have terrific shooters. If they were a business, they'd be a differentiated product. Other teams focus on playing great defense. In business, defense is like being the lowest cost provider. It doesn't mean you can completely abandon one in favor of the other, but you have to decide where to direct your focus. Does every player on your team know your strategy? I've talked to the Shockers' coach, and it's probably no surprise they primarily work on offensive drills in practice."

Dots were connecting for me. "I think I finally understand the Warren Buffett quote that you sent earlier this week. You either have to be the lowest cost producer or build up a brand that lets you charge more if you want to earn higher returns."

"That's correct," Mr. X said. "It always amazes me how Mr. Buffett can take a difficult concept and make it straightforward in so few words." *Might that be the very definition of wisdom?*

The home team had chipped away at the lead. By halftime, they were only down eight points. Mr. X told me it was well within striking distance for the Shockers potent offense. We took advantage of the reduced noise to continue the lesson.

"What about Cootie Burger?" I asked. "It seems like hamburgers are a commodity business. You can get a pretty good burger at a lot of different places these days."

"I'd agree, and because of that we are relentless with managing our costs. It's our primary area of focus. But we also strive to differentiate ourselves with a great customer experience. Remember the train from London to Paris that we talked about last time? Never forget to account for your customer's perception."

"That adds a lot more texture to the saying, *the customer is always right*,'" I said.

"It does," he said. "I'd modify that to say the customer's *experience* is always right. We look for ways to lower our expenses, but we do think there are some costs we incur that move the *Value* straw enough to justify the resources. I have bad news for you: none of this is strictly black and white. It's a spectrum with lots of gray and fuzzy measurement. But it helps to have a framework like this so you understand what you're trying to accomplish in your business."

"I have a question," I said. "With all of the new technology coming out all the time, how do you know if what you plan on delivering to customers will even move their *Value* straw? How can you keep up in such a rapidly changing world?"

"It's a fair question," he replied. "The answer is, you never really know for sure. There's a saying that no business plan survives first contact with the customer. And often, the customer can't even articulate the value they're feeling because it's happening at deeply subconscious levels. We're more like animals than we care to admit. There are a few clues though."

"Like what?" I asked.

"First, remember that technology is just a tool to accomplish a human want or need. Read up on Maslow's Hierarchy to see a nice organization of those desires. We have basic needs like food, shelter, clothing, connection, meaning, contribution. How we get our needs met will change based on the tools and technology of our time."

"OK, what else?"

"Second, in general the longer we humans have been using a particular technology, the longer we are likely to continue using it in the future. There's a persistence. It's very likely that humans will be watching a basketball game on Mars someday, and they'll still be sitting on chairs very much like these and using a fork to eat their food." *Ha, imagine all the technology required to set foot on another planet, yet you'd still use a chair and silverware to eat when you got there. What ever happened to the spork?*

"I hope the Martian seats are a little more comfortable than these," I said shifting around.

"True," he said. "They make my back hurt. But you can't beat the view."

"You're right," I said. "I never realized how tall they all are in person. Seeing them on TV is misleading."

"Their athleticism is remarkable," he said. "And less than one percent of them will make it to the professional level. They're here for the love of the game."

The Shockers came out of halftime on fire. The crowd energy swelled to a fever pitch as they made their run. The ball movement was breaking down the defense and leading to easy scoring opportunities. Before the visitors knew it, they were the team down eight points. Mr. X was confident this would happen all along. He had said the ball movement would eventually wear down the defense, like a boxer working the body, and he was right.

My teacher rearranged the straws back to their original configuration. "What if you had a low cost, provided a lot of value, and could control your price? What some might call having market pricing power. Slide price around and see if anything jumps out at you."

He went back to the game while I fumbled around with the straws. I slowly moved the *Price* straw back and forth between the *Cost* and *Value* straws. I noticed that the profit and brand wedges would grow or shrink depending on where the price was.

I caught a spark. "It looks like there's a trade-off between profit and brand. When the *Price* straw is near the *Cost* straw, there isn't much profit, but there's a lot of brand."

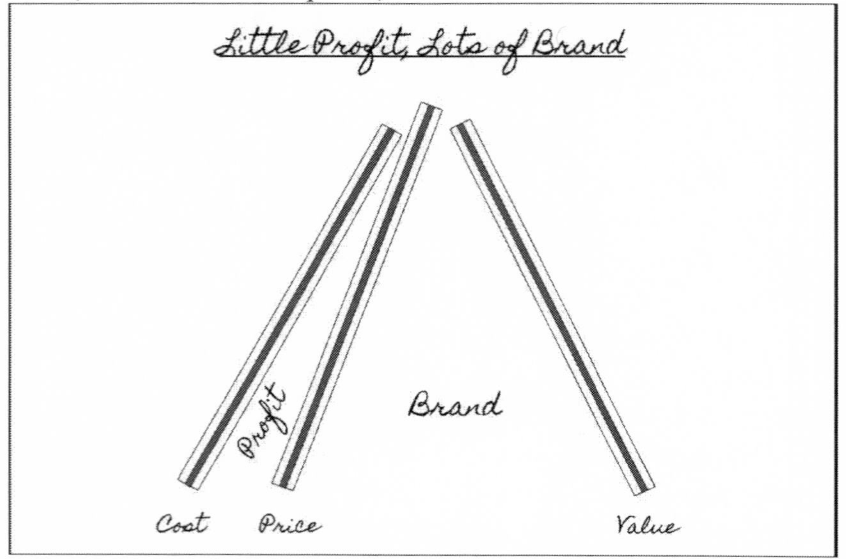

"When the *Price* straw is near the *Value* straw, there's a lot of profit, but not much brand. So even if you have pricing power and it seems like you can charge whatever you want, you're still making a tradeoff between profit and brand?"

"Very good," Mr. X said. *There was that odd glow inside again--why?* "The more profit a company generates, the more attention they draw to themselves. Competition, government regulators, even customers who might start to suspect they might be getting overcharged. True monopolies try to downplay their dominance and avoid looking greedy. Like slow-playing a winning hand in poker." *Am I being paranoid, or was that a subtle hint that he knew my true motivations?*

I stared at the straws, moving the price slowly back and forth in thought. "An analogy just hit me, Mr. X. I've always been fascinated by the human body. I probably should have been a doctor or something."

"Probably not smart enough," Mr. X teased me without turning away from the game.

"Probably not," I said. "Anyway, the *Price* straw acting as a lever reminds me of the role of insulin in the body. This is oversimplified, but insulin is like a switch that tells the body to either burn fuel in your system now as glucose, or save that energy for later in the form of fat."

"Keep going...," Mr. X said.

"Well, depending on what you do with price, you create two options. You can decide to store the energy locally in the form of profits which are readily available to you, like glucose in your bloodstream. Or you can tuck the resource away as fat for later use in the minds of your customers as *brand*. It's harder to get to and unlock when it's stored as fat, but I imagine similar to the body, you can store a lot more value in your customers' minds than you can on your own balance sheet. Looking at the crowd, there's a lot of *brand* stored up around here," I said.

My fat-shaming joke missed because Mr. X didn't even crack a smile. He was deep in thought. "I've never thought of it that way," he finally said. "But I like that analogy. You know, accountants have tried to get at measuring those fat stores. They call it *goodwill*. The accountants are pretty good at measuring company profits--the glucose in your analogy. That's straightforward. Goodwill is harder. When one company buys another, the accountants add up the glucose, and anything in addition to that are marked as fat stores. The fat then gets added to the balance sheet under the title *goodwill*."

"I remember goodwill from accounting classes, but it never made much sense to me. So if there hasn't been a recent transaction, how do they measure goodwill? It could add up to almost anything, right?"

"That's right," he said. "It gets worse. The current accounting assumption is that for private companies, those fat stores decay slowly to zero over a period of ten years. They call it *amortization*. For public companies, they don't assume decay, but every year you have to run some accounting procedures to see if your fat stores depleted. If the results say yes, you have to write them down as gone."

"Forever, like liposuction?" I asked.

He chuckled, "Yes, but here's a hypothetical: what if you're eating at Cootie Burger and part of your subjective experience is due to feelings of nostalgia? Imagine you're a parent eating a burger with your kids and the experience brought you back to a fond childhood memory of enjoying the same great food with your parents? Remember, it's all about the customer's subjective experience and stored memories. Unfortunately for accounting, that which is important, can't always be measured."

"I can see why that would be impossible to untangle," I said. "How could you make rules that applied for every business situation? I almost feel sorry for the accountants."

"Don't, they bring a lot of the scorn upon themselves," Mr. X said.

By this time, the Shockers were comfortably in the lead and the outcome was no longer in question. Both teams had subbed in their B-teams. The crowd cheered to celebrate as the other team waived the white flag.

"The game's almost over," Mr. X said. "Let's discuss one more topic before you head back. Did you know that a company can actually *grow* out of business?"

"I must have misheard you. Did you say *go* or *grow...?*"

"*Grow* with an 'r,'" he replied. "You'll see it's not that complicated. It has to do with cash flow. Think of cash as the oxygen of a business. During normal times when cash is plentiful, it's easy to ignore and take for granted. But when it's suddenly missing, it's hard to think about much else."

"I've heard the same thing said about sex…" I said.

"Me too," Mr. X said. *The old codger appreciated a dirty joke.* "The way that cash moves around in a business is incredibly important. It's probably the number one thing that trips up small business owners. They think to themselves, 'I'm selling more everyday, why is there no money in the bank?'"

"That would be confusing," I said.

"Here's what's going on," he said. "You collect cash from your customers. You use cash to pay your vendors for inventory and your employees for their labor. Some businesses are able to collect cash from their customers very early, well before they have to make these other payments. So there's always money in the bank to meet their expenses. These are generally easier businesses to run from a cash standpoint. The more you grow, the more cash builds up. Can you guess what a bad cash flow business looks like?"

"Sure," I replied. "It'd be the opposite."

"Right, you have to pay everyone before the customer pays you. As that kind of business grows, it requires more and more cash to keep things running. You have to fund the widening gap. And sometimes you never get paid by the customer while you're still on the hook for all of the bills."

"Does that happen?" I asked. *Does the little guy ever get away with not paying?*

"Occasionally," he said. "You can see how you might *grow* your way right out of business and into bankruptcy. Especially if you had no way to borrow extra cash to make the timing work."

"Are companies that require a lot of cash bad businesses then?" I asked.

"Cash flow requirements don't make a business good or bad necessarily. Plenty of solid, profitable businesses have poor cash characteristics. You just have to know what kind of business you're in so you don't get surprised and caught short. It helps to be conservative. When people forget they're in a bad cash business, the universe has a way of painfully reminding them."

The horn sounded and the game was over. We meandered toward the exits. Once outside, Mr. X gave me a curt goodbye and hailed a taxi. *So much for pleasantries.*

I caught my own cab back to the airport, already excited for my next visit. *Why wasn't school this enlightening or fun?*

CHAPTER 22

I tried to keep my trips to Wichita a secret. Yet it didn't take long before word had spread both at Big Rock and school. Coworkers and classmates pumped me for information. Everyone wanted to know what Mr. X was like. What does a billionaire do with his time? What does he spend money on? Did he give me any investing tips that could make *them* filthy rich? I wasn't sure how to tell them he was like their grandpa. He didn't go for leisurely swims in a money bin. He didn't have wads of hundreds in a suitcase guarded by Oddjob. People forgot that most of his wealth was tied up as ownership of his company, which no one could see.

I pretended to be annoyed by all of the questions, but I secretly delighted in the attention. I had spent a lot of my life going unnoticed. It felt good to have others want to talk about what I was doing. It fed my expanding ego. Impromptu huddles would break out at work and school. Me, ringed in the center, telling stories of my trips. *There's a fine line between good storytelling and embellishment.*

There was another reason I liked the attention: it really bothered Vance. He was accustomed to being the center of the universe. *Petty of me, I know. I wish I could say I was better than that.* I couldn't help myself from smiling inwardly at the look of disgust on Vance's face when I was holding court. I figured it might be good for his self-development to get knocked down a peg or two.

Although it operated as an old boy's club, Big Rock liked to think of itself as a meritocracy. In that spirit, the company would host regular internal competitions. They were looking for big ideas that might improve Big Rock. *Read: make Big Rock more money.* The contestants had to formally present their concepts to the higher-ups and they would decide who won. Anyone was technically eligible to participate, although the winners always came from the group you'd expect--those with the right last names. The prize was usually some new piece of electronics or a fun weekend getaway.

I had a midterm project due for my Budgeting and Controls class, so I figured why not use the same materials to pitch Big Rock. Mr. X had turned me onto zero-based budgeting, "ZBB" for short. We had never covered it at school, and best I could tell, it wasn't practiced at Big Rock. I didn't have the right family name to win, but it might be worth a try?

The prize this time was a trip for two to Catalina Island. With my meager salary, my bank account was goose eggs after the crushing student loan payments and sending money to my parents. The chance to take Stephanie on a classy getaway was worth the effort, even if the odds were low and I was petrified of public speaking.

CHAPTER 23

Before my next trip out to Wichita, I received the customary cryptic note from Mr. X. This time it was from that old economics guy, Adam Smith. *Not to be confused with the lead singer of any British cult bands.*

> *"What is prudence in the conduct of every private family can scarce be folly in that of a great kingdom."*

OK... your guess is as good as mine.

As instructed, I took a taxi from the airport to Cootie Burger headquarters. I recognized the parking lot and beige, nondescript building from my first visit. It was odd how nothing had changed, yet it felt like I had changed a lot since I was here last. It reminded me of a quote I'd read from an ancient philosopher: "No man ever steps in the same river twice, for it's not the same river and he's not the same man." *Deep thoughts, with Jack Handy.*

Cathy greeted me with a Midwest bearhug outside of the elevator before escorting me in. "I have to apologize up front that he might seem distracted today," Cathy said. "It could be a short session. He has an important, last-minute doctor's appointment today. We're waiting on test results that will give a better indication how much time he might have left." Her hushed tones failed to hide the emotions welling to the surface.

"That's OK. Sounds important," I said, trying to make her not feel bad that I'd just spent hours on an airplane. Compared to an ailing billionaire, my time wasn't worth much.

Cathy led me passed the conference room where Mr. X had wowed us on my first visit. We eventually reached a closed door at the end of the hall. Cathy knocked and pushed the door open slowly. "Mr. X? Nick is here."

"Hi, Mr. X," I said. He didn't look up as I entered.

"I'll leave you two alone," Cathy said, closing the door behind me.

Mr. X's office was nothing to write home about. It was a bright day outside, yet the room was dark with closed wooden slat blinds covering the large windows. The walls and carpet were ugly, Soviet-cast-off grays. A well-worn brown desk jutted out from the wall and faced the door. Opposite the desk were two chairs and a couch around a low-slung coffee table. Behind the desk on the back wall was a dull filing cabinet that provided more flat surface. On this were scattered picture frames and Cootie Burger memorabilia. There was probably a great story behind every piece, but they were just a little too far away for me to make out discernable details. On the desk sat a phone, a collection of binders, stacks of books, paper piles, and an empty inbox. *Why does the inbox have TOO HARD stenciled on it?* Conspicuously absent from his desk was any computer. The whole space looked more like the office of a struggling insurance salesman than a billionaire titan of industry. I felt a little better about my own sloppy desk at work.

Mr. X sat behind the desk, reading a report. Without looking up, he motioned for me to take a seat at one of the chairs in front of him. I waited for what seemed an uncomfortably long time while he finished reading. He looked more frail than at last visit's basketball game, and alarmingly pale.

Eventually he looked up. "You made it," he said. His smile surprised me with its warmth. It was like he really didn't know how long I had been sitting there waiting.

"Yes, sir," I said.

"Let's make the most of our time before I have to kick you out," he said. "Hopefully Cathy told you I have an appointment that might cut our time short?"

"She did," I said. "I wish it were under better circumstances."

"That makes two of us," he said. "I'd like to pick up where we left off last time, only with a few more advanced ideas. Then at the end, we can cover some biography items to give you some color that you're probably looking for."

"Great, but what we did last time wasn't advanced?" I asked.

"I'm as surprised as you are that you've kept up so far," he said. *I'd always hated being teased, but for some reason I didn't mind it from the old man.* He opened a nearby desk drawer and pulled out his now familiar straws and a sheet of paper.

"I guess you don't go anywhere without those," I said.

He only smiled while arranging his teaching aids. He wrote down cost, price, value, profit, and brand where I expected. "Here's the next lesson," he said, turning the diorama toward me. "You can use these straws to look at a business on a per unit basis at the individual transaction level. Say a customer buying one hamburger. You can look at it on the single store level in the case of one Cootie unit selling five hundred thousand hamburgers per year. Or you can also look at the entire Cootie enterprise selling hundreds of millions of hamburgers across the whole system."

I thought for a moment before responding. "Is it kinda like looking at the same thing at different levels of magnification? Like say through a microscope or binoculars or a telescope?" I asked.

It was his turn to think for a moment. "That's not a bad analogy," he said.

"I think I can already see what your Adam Smith quote from earlier this week might be about. If every family handles their own business smartly, it's likely to work out well for the whole kingdom," I said.

"Good, we can imagine our business at the various levels: the individual, the family, or the kingdom," he said. "Look at the diagram. Let's imagine the binoculars version where we're looking at the single store level. How could we lower the costs specifically at the store level?"

"Use low-quality meat, hire less staff, use scratchy napkins…"

Mr. X. cut me off, "... without impacting the perceived value for the customer."

"Oh," I said. "That would be tougher. There must be a clue that you started at the restaurant level and not the individual customer level." He nodded with approval.

"Here's a hint," he said. "One of the most important metrics for a restaurant, or any retail store for that matter, is called *same store sales*." *As if that were much of a clue, Mr. X.*

A few more beats of silence until he grumbled to my rescue, "You can lead a horse to water… OK, there are certain costs you pay every day whether you have one customer or one thousand. Think of the cost of the building, the electricity, the parking lot. They're conventionally known as 'fixed costs.' If we spread these costs across more customers, we actually lower the cost on a per-individual basis. That's why same store sales are so important. Do you follow?"

Mr. X slid the cost straw over in a ratcheting fashion to mime the effects. I nodded to him to keep going.

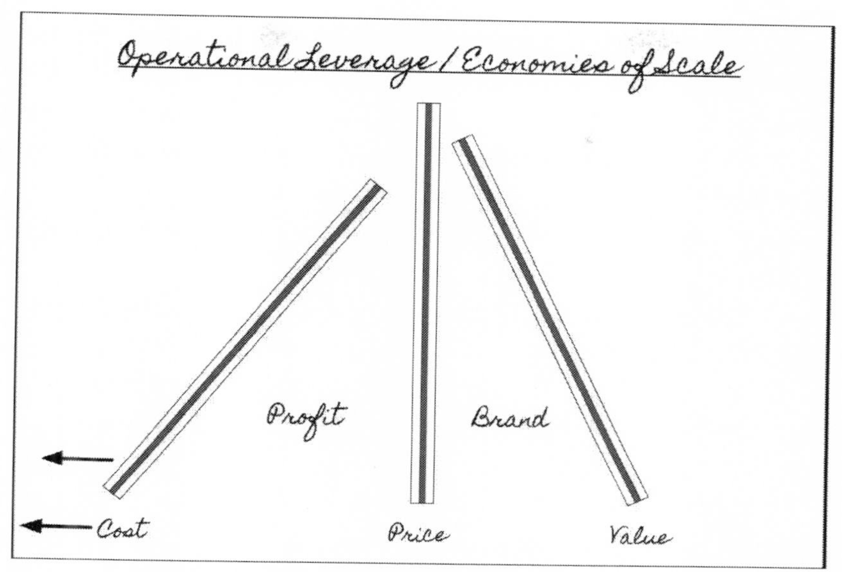

"You're increasing your profitability with every burger you sell," he said. "That gives you the option to collect more profit by leaving price where it is, or lower your prices to bank that value as brand in your customers' minds. More stored fat in your analogy. By the way, this concept of spreading fixed costs is referred to as *operational leverage* or *economies of scale*."

I smiled at his adoption of my fat analogy and the off-chance that I had made a contribution. "I can see a problem already," I said. "What happens if it reverses and fewer people are coming to your restaurant?"

"Great observation," he said. "Your fixed costs now have to be spread over a smaller pool of customers, so they go up on a per-customer basis. You not only lose the margin of the additional burger you might have sold. You accelerate toward declining profitability with each tick down in same store sales."

"So it's a double-edged sword then?" I asked.

"Yes, hence the name 'leverage,'" he said. "It can mean huge success on the way up, or a death spiral on the way down. So the single restaurant is found looking through binoculars magnification. How about that same concept looking through the telescope?"

"That's not too difficult to figure out," I said. "I assume you don't stay here rent free. I'd also guess that you and Cathy get salaries."

"They're modest, but we do," he said. *Sure, billionaire 'modest'?*

"The costs at headquarters are like the fixed cost of the four walls of a restaurant at the single store level. You can spread them out and dilute them across a larger number of burgers at the kingdom level." *Check out the big brain on Brad.*

"I think you're ready for the next lesson," Mr. X said. *No confetti dropping from the ceiling for my efforts?* "Here's your hint: look through your telescope at the *Value* straw and think about a fax machine."

"What?!" I thought to myself. *Or maybe I blurted out--who knows.* I refocused and buckled down, willing the diagram to offer me an answer. I couldn't get over how much of the business world he could explain with a few straws and a piece of paper. I felt a long way from the endless spreadsheets of Big Rock. And even farther from the complex formulas of academia that I would memorize just long enough to take the test before wiping the old hard drive. Someone could always break out the straws if they were having trouble solving a business problem.

"I've got it!" I said in a eureka moment. "One fax machine by itself provides no value. It's a paper weight. But as more get connected, the value of yours goes up a little bit because you can now exchange with more people. Eventually if there are fax machines distributed all over the world, they become incredibly useful as a network." I ratcheted the *Value* straw out to the right, mimicking each fax machine being added.

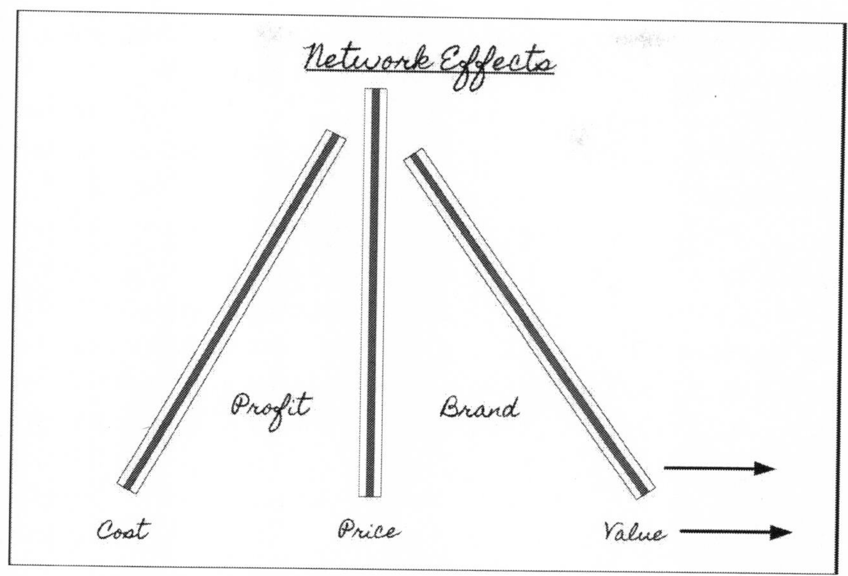

"That's right," he said. *There's that warm and fuzzy feeling I found myself craving.* "The fancy term is called *network effects*. Each unit you add at the individual level increases the value for everyone at the global network level. So you bump up everyone's *Value* straw at a faster rate than the costs grow. That's a pretty neat way to widen the gap between *Value* and *Price*, huh?"

"Yeah, but it seems like that's a rare instance for most businesses. Are there any network effects for Cootie Burger?" I asked.

"Perhaps, but it's not as obvious as the fax machine," he said. "It has to do with human psychology and how our brains work. We evolved in tribes and the default is to look at what the group is doing to see what's right and safe. So if you came into a busy Cootie Burger, each customer and burger sold would be social proof that this is a good, safe place to eat."

"At least no one was dying eating there," I kidded.

"You joke," he said. "But it's hardwired into our brains for survival. If you saw other people congregating near a watering hole, it must be safe from predators. What's interesting about humans is that expectations can affect your perceived experience. We're talking literally how your brain interprets the electrical signals from the taste buds in your tongue." *How did he have time to learn about this kind of stuff and still count his billions?*

He continued, "If you had been primed to expect a great meal: the cleanliness of the restaurant, smiling faces, it's likely you'd report it tasting better than if you ate by yourself in a dim, dirty shack. So for Cootie, each hamburger sold might subtly bump up the *Value* for every customer. At least that's my working theory," he said.

"A lot more of the world is subjective than I realized," I said.

"You have no idea," Mr. X said.

"I have a question, if we have time," I said.

"Better make it quick if we're going to cover biography stuff," Mr. X admonished.

"I can see how delivering a lot of value to your customers is important. But how do you measure that value? Are there any metrics? How would I know where my *Value* straw actually is?"

"That's a great question," he said. "Unfortunately, I don't have a great answer for you. First, that value is subjective in each customer's mind. This makes comparison and metrics very difficult. One way is to do customer feedback surveys, which come in many different flavors."

"I hate it when a business asks me to fill out a survey," I said.

"Most people do. That's the problem with surveys. You only get really happy or really angry customers who will invest the time to fill one out. The sampling bias makes most surveys questionable," Mr. X said.

"So you miss most of the people in the middle?" I asked.

"Right, it's far from a perfect science. But that shouldn't stop you from trying. The best one I've found so far to produce a single number is a method called *Net Promoter Score*. We use it at Cootie to ballpark the health of our *Value* straw. At least we can track changes over time. We ask the customer one simple question: 'On a scale of one to ten, how likely would you be to recommend us to a friend?' This question lets us group people into three buckets. The nines and tens are loyal, enthusiastic fans. They tell everyone they know and buy more as repeat customers. They're the lifeblood of any business. We can't get enough of them."

"Superfans," I said.

"Yes, into the next bucket go the sevens and eights. They're mildly satisfied. They aren't unhappy, but they aren't spreading the word about us either. And if they are, they aren't exactly glowing. They're more likely to be wooed away by a competitor."

"They're lukewarm," I said.

"The last bucket are the zero through six scores. They're the detractors. They spread negative word of mouth and are quick to leave if they think another company can do a better job. We try to avoid creating these, as they can be really damaging."

"The haters," I said.

"Is that what the kids would say these days?" he asked. "Anyway, after we get this simple number from the customer and put them into the three buckets, we then ask them an open-ended 'Why?' The whole system is designed to keep our own biases out of the measurement. We get feedback on what is working for customers and what is not. It's a treasure trove."

"Didn't you say this produces a single score?"

"Yes, and here's how we calculate it," he said. "We take the percentage who voted either nine or ten, then subtract the percentage who voted zero through six. We throw out the lukewarm sevens and eights. That number is the *Net Promoter Score* as we measure it."

"Let me see if I follow," I said. "Say you surveyed ten people. Five of them ranked you a nine or ten--they love you. Two of them were lukewarm sevens. Three of them said you stink and gave you a zero. Fifty percent minus thirty percent, throw away the lukewarms. Your Net Promoter Score is twenty."

"I thought you said you weren't good at math," he said.

"Very funny."

"Keep in mind, it varies by industry and customer demographics, but the typical score is in the thirty to forty percent range. A business that's doing a stellar job satisfying customers can be up in the seventies."

"What does Cootie Burger typically score?" I asked.

"For our industry, I'm happy with anything over fifty," he said. "A word of caution: you have to be careful comparing yourself only within your industry. A customer doesn't care if you're the best in the industry you're classified in. That means nothing to them. They care about how well you're solving one of their problems. As the saying goes, 'People don't want a half-inch drill bit. They want a half-inch hole in something.'"

"So it might be better to measure yourself against all of the competitors who are meeting a certain need, not some arbitrary industry classification?" I asked.

"Exactly," he said. "I'll give you an example. In the early days, who was Southwest Airlines biggest competition?"

"Delta or United?" I guessed.

"Nope. Here's a hint: Southwest focused on short trips between smaller cities."

"Hmm… smaller regional airlines?" I said. I couldn't name any of them.

"No, don't be so orthodox," he said.

I thought for a quiet beat. Who moved people between small cities? Then it hit me like a bus: "Greyhound!"

"That's right," Mr. X said. "Southwest was competing against Greyhound Bus Lines in the early days. Flying Southwest was obviously a major upgrade from taking a bus, so they were able to dominate that niche before they ever had to worry about taking on the entrenched big boys like Delta or United. The broader point here is that you need to be crystal clear with which human need you're addressing. Measure yourself against others addressing that same need."

"That makes sense," I said.

"Of course it does," he said. "Now, you have five minutes to ask me about my life or else I'm going to be late for my doctor's appointment."

I looked through my notes searching for something easy to get him warmed up. "You've already told the story of your father passing away and you taking over the business. What was your mindset in those early years of being in charge?"

"Survival. Next question," he said.

"Umm, let's see," I said as I paged through. "How did you meet your wife?"

"At church. Next question." *Is he stonewalling me or just being efficient?*

"Tell me about your daughter," I said. I knew it was a delicate question, but I wanted to shake him up a little.

He was quiet for a few beats. "She's amazing--takes after her mother. I love her and it breaks my heart that we aren't speaking."

"When did…" I started, but he cut me off.

"That's all the time we have today. I have to get to my appointment. Cathy will make sure you get to the airport. See you in a few weeks."

And with that, this trip to Wichita was over. *That definitely wasn't five minutes. Why were his answers so curt? Did he not trust me? He would talk about business all day, but the personal side was one-word answers. What gives?*

CHAPTER 24

Every year Big Rock threw a large gala for the employees. Heavy appetizers and even heavier booze. It gave the higher-ups a chance to assemble and congratulate each other on being masters of the universe. Us lowly peons were invited to eat a few shrimp and look on in admiration.

I invited Stephanie to be my plus one, but I was nervous. I wasn't sure how she'd react to the frat boy culture of Big Rock, especially after adding dangerous levels of alcohol to the flowing testosterone. *And if I'm being honest, I was worried about being the butt of every emasculating joke in front of my girlfriend. The girlfriend deflector shields can only withstand so many photon torpedoes before your manhood comes into question. (They can only stand so many nerdy Star Trek analogies as well.)* I thought about the quiet serenity of our nature hikes that were so magical. This event would be the exact opposite: loud, crowded, and fake. My cortisol level spiked just thinking about the social minefield.

I picked Stephanie up before the party. She looked simply stunning. I almost didn't recognize her at first. She wore a little black dress and more makeup than I'd seen before. It was like that cliche movie scene where the mousy girl takes off her glasses and lets her hair down to reveal a beauty queen. I shouldn't have been surprised. Whenever I started to think I had her figured out, she had a deeper layer or another gear. There was always more below the surface.

Based on the noise level, we arrived about three drinks in. We filled up our plates with hors d'oeuvres, grabbed two glasses of something cold and stiff, and found a place to sit away from the main fray. I dished dirt on all of my co-workers as we people-watched. The water cooler never wanted for salacious material at Big Rock; I had ample stories to share. We were having fun in our own little bubble. After we'd finished our plates, I left her at the table to fetch fresh drinks.

I returned to a nightmare. Vance was sitting next to Stephanie at the table, along with two of his closest Big Rock cronies and their two dates. *What, no supermodels joining us tonight, Vance? Awww, poor fella.* Based on his body language and proximity to Stephanie, it didn't take a genius to figure out what Vance's plans were. *That mother....*

I walked up to the table, mustering up all of the faux confidence I had. In my head, George McFly was stuttering, *"Get your damn hands off her."*

Vance saw me coming and didn't miss his chance. "Oh good, we'll take another round of Manhattans, boy." The cronies thought this was hilarious.

"Very funny, Vance." I said.

I was checkmated by the seating arrangements. I had the option of hovering near Vance and Steph--the awkward third wheel. Or there was a free seat on the far side of the table. Of course, Vance didn't offer to vacate my chair. That seat was his birthright. I banished myself to social Siberia on the other side of the table to avoid confrontation. *Like a total wuss.*

I ignored the vapid conversation of the cronies and their girls. I kept my eyes on Stephanie and Vance who were having their own conversation. It was too noisy for me to hear what they were saying, but I was looking for clues. Did she need my help? It didn't seem like it. I watched her laugh at something he said, a jealous green acid coursing through my veins. Did she like Vance? He was tall, handsome, and suave. Who wouldn't like him? Was she thinking about trading up from a dented Camry to the high-end Ferrari? I was deflated and wondering how many drinks it would take to render me oblivious to this mess. *Bartender...*

Vance leaned in close to whisper something. Stephanie's body went rigid and a sour look crossed her face. Vance touched her arm and she pulled away.

Something in me snapped.

Without thought, I shot out of my chair and was around the table in a flash. Vance popped out his chair and we were suddenly face to face. Nevermind that Vance had 4 inches and at least thirty pounds of muscle on me. The scent of alcohol on his breath brought me back to the reality that I was way outside my weight class.

"What are you doing?" I seethed.

"None of your business, bro. Don't you have some trees to plant or whales to save?"

"What did you say to her?" I said.

"Who cares? She's not my type anyway. You can have her," he said. *She's too good for you.*

In my mind, I reached back to punch him. Then I saw myself in a ball on the ground, Vance and his cronies kicking me like they were on the pitch at the World Cup. I saw myself getting fired from Big Rock for punching their Golden Boy. I saw myself homeless under a bridge, sharing a can of beans with my parents.

I felt Stephanie pull on my arm. "C'mon, Nick."

I could only think in shredded fragments with all my swirling rage. We walked off, my fists clenched, white hot anger my only impulse. Over my shoulder I heard Vance say, "That's what I thought."

I almost turned around and hit "play" on the scenario that would lead to my world imploding. But Stephanie squeezed my arm assuringly and I kept walking. My adrenalized tunnel vision made it hard to do anything but put one foot in front of the other. The rage slowly drained.

We made the rounds so I could introduce Stephanie to my bosses and get credit for having been at the gala. It was a tactical error not to have done so earlier in the night. The bosses had rounded 'in the bag' and were headed toward blackout. I doubted my presence even registered. Oh well, I guess there's always next year. *If I don't get fired first.*

After an especially slurry and pawsy encounter, I asked Stephanie, "Are you ready to get outta here?"

"Yes, please," she said. Her eyes pleaded that she was done.

We couldn't get to the coat check fast enough.

CHAPTER 25

I received a Warren Buffett pre-trip trifecta from Mr. X:
-- *"While deals often fail in practice, they never fail in projections."*
-- *"The higher return a business earns on the capital that is invested in the business, the more cash it is producing and the more value is being created."*
-- *"Growth can destroy value if it requires cash inputs in the early years of a project or enterprise that exceed the discounted value of the cash that those assets will generate in later years. Growth is simply a component--usually a plus, sometimes a minus--in the value equation."*

I had no idea where Mr. X was leading with his quotes, but I kind of enjoyed the surprise of finding out.

Cathy had given me a time and address in Wichita where I was to meet Mr. X. When the taxi dropped me off at the nearest cross streets, I was surprised to see a silver RV shining in a vacant lot. The air was crisp and clear, carrying kitchen sounds and delicious smells from the truck. The rig was branded with sharp Cootie Burger markings. I finally recognized the RV for what it really was: a Cootie-themed food truck. The line to order was at least ten deep. Several wooden picnic tables held patrons enjoying burgers and fries. At the farthest table, I saw the old man surreptitiously observing the scene. I walked over and sat down across from him.

"Hi, Mr. X," I greeted.

"What do you think of this operation?" he asked, his eyes still studying.

"It's making me hungry, if that's your question," I said.

"Good, I took the liberty of ordering you a burger and fries. It should be out shortly now that you've arrived."

"Wow, thanks. Are you going to eat?" I asked.

"I'm not very hungry these days," he said. He smiled meekly before coughing into a handkerchief.

"I bet. How did your tests go last week?"

"Not well, actually. But what do doctors know, right?" *Fighting the good fight.* "How would you feel about the same procedure as last time? I'll teach at the beginning and then you can ask me some personal questions."

"Sure thing," I said.

"Let's get started then," he said, all business. "About twenty percent of the funding a company uses comes from *external* financing. Do you know where the other eighty percent comes from?"

"I'm going to take your hint and guess it's *internal* financing?" I said.

"I spoonfed you that one--but what does 'internal' really mean?" he said.

"Money that comes in from just the course of doing business?" I offered.

"OK, but let's see if we can improve on that," he said. "I would modify to say it's taking all of the inputs, combining them in some magical way, and being able to sell the result for more than it costs. Remember back to our straws. What was the triangle that was formed by the *Price* and *Cost* straws?"

After all of the practice, it was easy to reconstruct the straws in my mind's eye. "Profit, Mr. X."

"Good, you haven't forgotten," he said. "So eighty percent of a typical company's funding is financed through their own profits. In business school, they must have taught you about *return on invested capital*. R-O-I-C, for short."

"I'm not sure if we've gotten to it yet. Sounds like another acronym to add to the pile," I said.

"All it means is, for every dollar that's put into the business for operations, how much comes out?"

"That's it?" I said.

"Yes, sir," he said. "So if you put a dollar into a business, and it throws off fifty cents of profit, what was your return on invested capital?"

"Fifty percent," I said. "That seems pretty straightforward."

"Typically for a public company, ROIC is measured in yearly increments," Mr. X said before coughing violently into his handkerchief.

I gave him some time to recover before I asked, "What is Cootie's ROIC?"

"Sorry, this damn cough," he apologized. "For Cootie? Last year it was twenty-one percent."

"Is that good?"

"We have a good business. The historical ROIC in the U.S. is around 6%, but that can vary widely any given year and by industry," he said.

"Cootie must be a great business then," I said. "Was last year typical?"

"That's slightly higher than normal, but not atypical. Any particular year is not how I like to think about it though. In spite of our desire for order, business usually doesn't map well to one trip around the sun."

"How do you like to think about it then?" I asked. I was starting to figure out how to ask questions that kept him engaged. *A regular billionaire tycoon whisperer.*

"Many companies will measure the ROIC of individual projects, which probably makes more sense than any given year. But internally at Cootie, we do something even more different."

"What's that, you rebel?" I said.

"We measure the ROIC of *strategies*," he said.

"Sorry, but what's the difference between a project and a strategy? They sound the same to me."

"A strategy is a bigger goal we're trying to accomplish as a team. If you recall our previous conversations, a good strategy for us involves finding ways to better delight our customers or lower our costs. There are usually several projects that make up a strategy. Like a bundle," he said.

"How about this for an analogy?" I said after a moment's thought. "A strategy is a direction you're hiking, like east or west, and the projects would be the different paths through the woods you can take to get there." *I must have had hiking with Stephanie in my subconscious.*

"That's a decent analogy. I might even start using that one," he said. He appeared to perk up at my catching on.

"I have my moments…"

"I haven't seen many," he said with a wink before continuing. "We prefer to assess and fund strategies and not individual projects for several reasons. First, we're aiming to succeed in the long term. A strategy is inherently more long term focused than a single project."

"Alright, I'll buy that," I said. A man from the food truck in crisp Cootie attire found his way to our table and placed a delectable burger and piping hot fries in front of me. He smiled earnestly and left, not wanting to interrupt.

"Please, go ahead and eat. I wish I was hungry. I'll keep talking though," Mr. X said. "Now… where was I?"

"Funding strategies instead of projects," I said with a mouth full of burger.

"Right," he said, frowning at my table manners. "There are important human dynamics to consider. Don't forget that it's people who are coming up with these ideas. It's easy to fudge the projections on individual projects and make the numbers work. Not due to any maleficence--it could be they're simply enthusiastic. Humans tend to be overconfident and extrapolate in straight upward lines when they get excited."

"The first Buffett quote makes sense now," I said between bites. "The projections never fail to show a profit."

"Very good," he said. "My view is that it's harder to overestimate an entire strategy. So thinking in strategies keeps the numbers more honest and your team pulling in the same direction."

"I see," I said.

"We pursue a strategy together, not pet projects that make an individual champion look good. Innovation is often best done in teams by combining ideas in novel ways. How's your burger?" he asked.

"Amazing!" I said. "I'm not sure why, but the fried egg really adds to the experience. Put me down for a nine Net Promoter Score."

"Why not a ten?" he asked.

"There's always room for improvement, right?" I said. "Anyway, back to our lesson. So the group is collectively aimed at going west, rather than focusing on any individual path to take?" I asked.

"Exactly," he replied. "It has a unifying effect. Here's another takeaway: thinking in strategies can open your eyes to new paths in the forest. Sometimes a great idea is staring you right in the face and you don't see it until you look at your bigger strategy."

"Can you give me an example of that at Cootie?" I said, looking for a concrete anchor point.

"Absolutely," he replied. "It's the very reason I had you meet me here. We have a *strategy* to lower the cost of testing restaurant locations."

"Did you and your team actually brainstorm together all the different ways you could lower the cost of testing?" I asked.

"Yes, we did," he said. "We have to determine *where* people want to eat our hamburgers. And any costs we can save figuring that out are meaningful. Those saved resources mean we have more left to test other projects and fund other strategies to lower costs or wow our customers."

"Being a good steward of capital," I said like a true teacher's pet. I still felt like the old man was keeping me at arm's distance.

He smiled, "Very good, Nick. Back to the testing. When we first started out, it was based on my gut feelings of different locations and communities. We'd build a new location, crossing our fingers it would work out--not very scientific at all. We got better by funding a project to measure traffic patterns to make better decisions. Then one day, one of our employees went on vacation to Disneyland. Los Angeles was the birthplace of the food truck scene and as soon as he saw one, he had a great idea. We could use food trucks to test out a location in small scale to see if our brand of burgers and shakes would be popular in an area."

"That's genius," I said.

"The employee was relatively low in our organization, but was eager to share his breakthrough. A good idea is a good idea; we encourage every employee to contribute their insights," he said. "We realized we could use food trucks to test locations without having to spend anywhere near the money required for a full restaurant build. A food truck costs about $60,000 to outfit. One of our restaurants is around $1.5 million to build. Granted, it's not a perfect correlation that a successful truck test will become a good permanent location. But a new truck is less than five percent the cost of a restaurant, and we can keep reusing the trucks."

"Right, because they're mobile," I said.

"Yes," he said as he coughed again. "It's worth the initial test, and sometimes the results surprise us. This project has easily saved us tens of millions by avoiding swings and misses. We could have put out over a million dollars to build a full restaurant that ended up with low traffic. Remember back to operational leverage? Our errors show up as bad returns on invested capital."

"So say, putting one dollar in and only getting two cents out?" I asked.

"Or even a negative number," he said. "Being bad stewards of capital."

"Is it that big of a deal?" I wondered aloud. "After all, you still have the restaurant you built."

"Some CEOs would have you believe it's not," he said. "But a positive or negative ROIC is a huge deal when you look at the entire capitalistic ecosystem. Misallocation is bad for the company because we have less profits to reinvest. Where's the internal eighty percent of funding going to come from? It's bad for customers because we built in a location no one really wanted. It's bad for the environment because we wasted materials and energy for a building that will likely be torn down. It's bad for society because not making progress is a waste of everyone's time and talent."

"Wow," I said. "A positive or negative ROIC tells you all of that?"

"Isn't it amazing how when you view the world through this lens, capitalism puts everyone on the same team? Capital allocation done well is good for everyone at different levels. We don't celebrate it enough." *I hate to admit it, but Mr. X was making some sense.*

"Why don't business people talk more about doing important work like that?" I asked.

"Some do," he said. "My hope is that most don't because they're just doing the work rather than talking about it. That might be generous though."

"I think I understand the second Buffett quote now," I said.

"Now there's a business person who gets it," Mr. X said.

"Higher returns on capital mean more value is being created. Not just for the business or investors, but for the whole ecosystem," I said, more to myself than to Mr. X.

"I think you're starting to appreciate the importance of the capital allocator job," he said. "It's always bothered me how under-recognized it is for the wellbeing of humanity. I know it sounds like hyperbole, but good business decisions can positively impact us more than nearly anything else."

We sat quietly for a time, both deep in thought. Mr. X's coughing continued. I was sympathetic, but felt helpless to do anything.

He calmed down and we continued. "I'm going to be coming to California next week for business, so you won't need to travel. I'll come see you," he said.

"That'd be great," I said. *My butt was suddenly relieved at the prospect of not being crammed into a middle seat again.*

"Let's keep the lesson going while I'm not coughing. There are some other big takeaways for ROIC. Especially when it comes to growing. Not all growth is good."

"It seems like a rapidly growing business is what everyone wants, right? It's all you hear in the press."

"There is a strange fascination with growth," he said. "Maybe a better term for growth would simply be "more." If you're doing something right, *more* is good. But if you're doing something wrong, *more* is definitely not what you want. Return on invested capital can serve as the gauge that tells you if you're doing something right or wrong."

"When you say *right or wrong*, what do you mean?" I asked.

"I mean, are you giving the consumer something they value and are you delivering it in a cost effective manner? Think back to our straws," he said.

"*C-P-V*. You have to be delivering more value than you charge. You have to charge more than it costs to produce," I said.

"That right, ROIC tells you how effective you are."

"I follow," I said.

"Here's a story to help you remember the dynamic between growth and return on invested capital. As a young man I sent away for Charles Atlas's exercise program. It got me into training with heavy weights. You seem like you're in pretty good shape. Do you ever lift weights?"

"Not really. I'm more of a runner," I said. I suddenly felt self-conscious of my underdeveloped upper body.

"You're at least familiar with the bench press exercise?" he asked.

"Yes." *I'd always stayed away from it after imagining myself succumbing to gravity and being choked to death by the bar. What a way to go.*

"Imagine the bench press," he said. "During my Atlas training, I learned you need to use proper form to avoid injury. Before you load up the bar with heavy weights, you must have your form correct, usually through practice with lighter weights. Does that make sense?"

"Sure, train with lighter weights until you get the right movement down. That's why show-offs end up hurting themselves." *I wonder how much Vance can bench?*

"That's right," he said. "In this analogy, your return on invested capital is your form. It shows you how well your product or service fits with what consumers want. Only after you have proper form as demonstrated through sufficient returns should you attempt to add the extra plates of growth and scale up."

"So you do smaller scale testing to make sure you have adequate returns on capital before you try to scale up and grow?" I said.

He nodded. "What happens if you add too much weight without developing proper form?"

"You get hurt," I said.

"Similarly, if you attempt growth without showing adequate returns on capital, you wind up destroying value and risking business injury, even death," he said.

"Makes sense," I said.

"It does, but you'd be surprised how uncommon it is in practice," he said.

"I understand the third Buffett quote now. Growth can destroy value if it isn't earning a return on investment," I said. *It was satisfying when the puzzle piece clicked into place. The old man was a pretty good teacher.*

"Stop me if you've heard this one," Mr. X said. "Some businesses lose a little bit on every transaction… but they make it up in volume!" He chuckled to himself as was his nature.

"I've heard that before, but I never understood enough to appreciate it," I said.

"Would you like to hear a practical example for ROIC?" he asked.

"Yes, please. I do better with the practical."

Mr. X continued, "For a long time, we kept everything in-house by building and running our own restaurants. As you can imagine, it takes quite a bit of money to buy a promising piece of land. Then we had to use more money to put up a structure and add all of the restaurant equipment. We were decent at developing these real estate projects that would turn into good sites for restaurants. It required a lot of money to grow, which kept us expanding slowly. We ended up with a lot of capital tied up in real estate. And the long run return on real estate is closer to three percent. See anything wrong here?" he said. *He loved to bait the hook and test me.*

I thought for a second, picking at a few fries that were left over. "Wait, didn't you say earlier that Cootie earned around twenty percent returns on capital?"

"I did," he said. "Keep going, you're on the right track."

"Well, if most of your capital was tied up in real estate earning around three percent, how do you get up to twenty percent?" I asked.

"Bingo! I asked myself the same question: how can we get better returns on our capital? Said another way, where was our organization able to create the most value for our customers, all while consuming the least resources? I made a surprising discovery. We weren't the best at the real estate side of value creation. We shined when it came to sourcing quality ingredients, crafting an enjoyable customer experience, and strict attention to detail in operations. We were simply better at logistics than real estate. Remember, it's a fool's errand to believe that you can be good at everything," he said.

"I've paid attention to the behind-the-counter operation at Cootie--it's very impressive," I said.

"Thank you, that's decades of iteration at work, one-percent at a time. We figured out we were more effective by focusing on what we were really good at--restaurant operations. We now let others help with the real estate side of the equation. Do you know what 'franchising' is?"

"I've heard of it, but I probably couldn't explain it to someone very well," I said.

"The definition of a franchise is the right to use a firm's business model or brand. They had a form of franchising back in the Middle Ages, but it wasn't until the 1960s that the concept really gained popularity," Mr. X said.

"The franchisee, whom we carefully screen, has responsibility for the real estate side of the business. They get help from us on the operations and get to use the Cootie name and systems. In exchange, we get a percentage of their restaurant's revenue. Cootie makes more money with less invested capital through franchising. Our invested capital goes into designing better systems and building our brand--not buying more real estate. That's how our returns on invested capital are around twenty percent and not three percent."

"It sounds like you're leaving the franchisee the short end of the stick?" I said. *Aha! The first slip up. He must be screwing over the franchisees. That's capitalism for you, someone's always getting shafted.*

"Not really," he replied. "The franchisee can leverage our decades of experience running restaurants. They make more money and earn a higher ROIC on their real estate than most of the other options they could do with that land. It's a win-win relationship. We only participate in arrangements where everyone wins." *Hmm, that didn't sound like Marx to me. I'll have to keep digging. He'll stumble eventually.*

"Wait, why do you need food trucks and company-owned restaurants then?" I asked.

"Good question," he replied. "We have to keep our finger on the customer pulse. We can't do that without testing. And you need to control the entire process from beginning to end to practice good science."

"I see--small scale testing," I said.

"It also allows us to put ourselves in our franchisees' shoes. If there's something we're struggling with, they're probably experiencing the same issue. It's all part of being a productive member in the ecosystem," he said. A coughing fit came over him that was worse than any of the previous. It was bad enough that some patrons looked on with concern. *How bad does it have to get before I call someone?*

"That's all I can do today," he said between coughs. "I need to get out of this cold. Can you take a raincheck on the personal questions this time?"

"Sure, you're the boss, Mr. X," I said.

"Will you call Cathy to pick me up, please?"

I dialed Cathy and told Mr. X I'd catch a cab back to the airport after she arrived. He thanked me between coughs. As we waited, I noticed the crimson blood on his handkerchief. *How much time did we have left?*

CHAPTER 26

Travel sounds romantic at first. Until you have to do it again. And again. It turns into a grinder of both soul and body. *Another crying baby on this flight?!* I was very happy to avoid the airplane as Mr. X came to visit California. He sent me a Warren and Charlie two-fer a few days before his trip.

> *"All financial assets can be made economic equals: It applies to outlays for farms, oil royalties, bonds, stocks, lottery tickets, and manufacturing plants. And neither the advent of the steam engine, the harnessing of electricity nor the creation of the automobile changed the formula one iota--nor will the Internet. Just insert the correct numbers, and you can rank the attractiveness of all possible uses of capital throughout the universe."*
>
> *-- Warren Buffett*
>
> *"In the real world, you uncover an opportunity, and then you compare other opportunities with that. And you only invest in the most attractive opportunities. That's your opportunity cost. That's how we make all of our decisions."*
>
> *-- Charlie Munger*

The old man wanted to see my campus. I had Mr. X and Cathy meet me on a corner near school. Cathy deposited him with me and bolted for a coffee shop to tackle her own work. I told them I had made a reservation for four at a nice restaurant tonight and I wanted them to meet my girlfriend Stephanie. Cathy, the keeper of the calendar, accepted enthusiastically.

Mr. X and I agreed we should take advantage of the nice California weather and walk around the campus for our meeting. Walking was a bit of an exaggeration. Mr. X now required the aid of a cane--doctor's orders. Apparently a fall at that age is a death sentence. He shuffled as he gingerly planted his cane with every step. I hovered close by just in case he needed extra help. I had plotted out a course that would steer us near the most scenic parts of the campus. Despite our slow pace, Mr. X's mind was as sharp as ever.

"Where does money come from in a business?" he asked innocently enough as we meandered through the brick buildings.

"Investors?" I guessed.

"That can be true, but I've always found the term 'investor' quite vague. Let's see if we can clear things up. Did you know that most of the time when someone invests in the stock market, the business doesn't see any of that money?" he said.

"Really?"

"No," he said. "That money goes to pay off the owner of the shares you're purchasing. You're buying her out of her position. She takes your cash; you take her shares. It's a trade." *Is his use of a female pronoun Cathy's influence? I appreciated his progressivism.*

"Remember though, the company doesn't see any of that money. They can't buy new equipment or pay employees just because you traded with someone. No new value is created. The stock market is what's called a *secondary* market. It's like a flea market for second hand goods," he said.

"Like eBay?" I asked.

"Like eBay, if you prefer," he nodded. "Except instead of Beanie Babies, you can swap ownership of public companies."

"OK, that's not quite as glamorous as Wall Street makes it sound," I said.

"Indeed," was all he added.

We made our way slowly toward a small pond, ringed with benches. Mr. X looked like he could use a break, so we staked out a spot to bask in the sun like lizards.

"Where do public shares come from to begin with?" he asked. He favored the Socratic method, which always made me think of "Bill and Ted's Excellent Adventure": *So-crates, watch out for your robe, dude.*

"The IPO?" I responded. *Let's hope he doesn't ask me to explain that process.*

"Very good, the company sells some or all of itself to the general public. It's still a trade. In this case, the founders and early investors get the money, and the public become new owners. Unfortunately, the track record of returns for investors buying IPOs is terrible."

"Really? Don't you hear in the news about a hot new IPO that everyone wants to invest in?" I asked. "I've seen articles that say, 'If you had bought company ABC at IPO, you'd be super rich.'"

"True, some end up working out, and occasionally, the returns for an investor are spectacular. But those home runs are few and far between and the odds are not in your favor. It's closer to playing the lottery. Let me ask you a question," he said.

"Shoot."

"Who knows more about the business and what it's truly worth: the public looking on from the outside, or the founders who built the company? Who knows the true upside or the hidden risks?" he asked.

"Obviously being on the inside, the founders must know more," I said.

"That's right. When you slave over a business for years to make it successful, it becomes your baby. Would the founder ever let go of her baby, unless the price was incredibly favorable for her?"

I shook my head no.

"And if it's favorable for her, wouldn't that by definition mean it's *unfavorable* for the other side of the transaction? In this case, Joe Public. The founders know where all of the bodies are buried," he said.

"It is hard to imagine them giving the little guy a deal for something they built," I said. "Why would they?"

"That's why buying an IPO is usually a loser's bet," he concluded. "Shall we keep walking, or are your legs too tired?" *What a joker.*

I helped him up and we continued our stroll. We walked under a large arch that was a well-known campus landmark. Young people walking by smiled; it looked like I was giving an elderly family member a tour. *My "grandfather" is richer than your grandfather.*

"Where does money come from to start a business?" Mr. X said.

"Well, it must be before the IPO because the business is already up and running," I said.

"Good, think really small," he encouraged. "Did you ever run a lemonade stand as a kid?"

"Sort of, for about two hours one summer. I got hot and bored and went inside to play Nintendo," I said.

Mr. X frowned and shook his head, maybe mockingly. "Where did the money come from for your lemonade stand? To buy the lemons and sugar?"

I tried to remember how things had happened. "I had a little bit of money saved up, plus I borrowed some money from my parents."

"So you were financed with both debt and equity?" he said.

"What..."

"I'm just teasing," he said. "You put in money as the owner of the business. You owned one hundred percent of the lemonade stand and were entitled to any profits it produced. Assuming you weren't too distracted by the video set," he said. *Old people never get tech names right. Is that out of active obstinance or just not caring to keep up with a changing world?*

He continued, "The money you borrowed from your parents--you had to pay them back eventually, right?" I nodded. "Since that money was only borrowed, they didn't own the lemonade stand with you. They weren't entitled to any profits. That borrowed money is called 'debt financing.' It accounts for about twenty percent of the external money businesses use if you look at the long term average in the United States," Mr. X said.

"What could I have done other than borrow money from them?" I asked.

"You could have brought your parents in as fellow owners. They give you money. You don't have to pay it back, but now they're in line with you when it comes time to pay owners. They become your business partner. That's called 'equity financing,'" he said.

"I've never heard those terms described so simply," I said. *The old man had a knack for distilling concepts that tangled my brain at work and school.* "So if my lemonade stand was a typical U.S. business, I'd put up eighty dollars of equity and my parents would put up twenty dollars of debt?" I asked.

"That's about right," he said. "Equity goes by different names depending on when it happens in the life of a business. They call it seed funding, angel investing, venture capital, IPOs, stock options, private equity. But the concept is the same: equity is ownership," he said.

"That finally makes sense," I said.

"There are a few other external sources of money for a business," he said as we walked. "You can borrow money from your vendors for short periods of time. Here's how that works: you get the lemons you need now, but don't have to pay for them for thirty days. Vendor financing is usually short-lived, but it can be an important source of cash for some companies," he said. His gait was slow, but his mind was still firing on all cylinders.

"I imagine that can work against you as well. Having to pay vendors before you get paid by your customers? *Growing* out of business," I said. *Whenever I could, I tied back to our past conversations to validate he wasn't wasting his time with me.*

"You're exactly right," he said. "There's another side of the coin. You can get money from your customers before you deliver your product or service to them. Are you old enough to remember layaway?"

"It sounds familiar," I said.

"It mostly went away when credit cards became popular. Back in the day, if you didn't have enough money to buy what you wanted, you could put money down as a deposit. You'd save up the rest, and when you could pay the difference, you got the product," he said.

"People must have been better at delaying gratification back in the olden days," I said.

"Clearly," he said. "There are other examples. Think about an insurance company. They take your money as premiums up front. Then if you later file a claim, they pay you out to cover whatever was insured. But in the meantime, they get to keep that money and invest it. It's called *float*. As in the customer is *floating* the insurance company money up front. When a good investor like Warren Buffett gets access to float, it can be a special combination. But most people aren't Warren Buffett..." he said.

"I just thought of another one," I said. "I saw on the counter that you have gift cards for Cootie Burger. The customer gives you the cash up front, then redeems it for food later. But in the meantime, you get to do whatever you want with the cash. Would that be considered float?"

Mr. X beamed, "Very clever! Yes, that is absolutely float. We're always interested in ways of taking in more cash before we have to pay it out. Gift cards are one way that makes sense for our business," he said. *Was I actually starting to understand business? Gasp, the horror! Quick, someone get me an antidote copy of "Das Capital."*

"I think I have another one," I said. "Are you familiar with crowdfunding? Basically, an entrepreneur pitches the idea for a product. Usually they have some kind of prototype, like an ice chest with a radio built into it or something. If people like it, they can make a small deposit as a commitment to buy. This gives the entrepreneur the money needed to at least get started in building the product. They get a built-in customer before they have to take the risk of large-scale production. Isn't that a form of borrowing from your customer?"

He stopped shuffling for a moment to think. "Hmm… it sounds an awful lot like layaway, but what you're describing could be considered float, sure. Once you understand the concept, you start to see it all over. That's what I love about business. There's always something new to learn," he said.

"Tell me about your proudest moment," I said. *It was my turn to steer the conversation for a while.*

"There have been so many over the years," he said. "So many business deals and breakthroughs. I've had a very fortunate run."

"How about the proudest moment in your personal life?"

"That'd be a three way tie: the day my wife and I tied the knot and the birth of each of my children."

"I've only heard you mention the one daughter," I said.

"I had a son as well, but that's a story for another time," he said coldly. *Hint taken: no trespassing.*

"What was your wife like?" I asked.

"'Lovely' is the only word that gets close," he said. "Kind and patient, with a quiet inner strength. She gave me a feeling that as long as she was in my corner, we'd be able to get through anything together."

"She sounds like a great life partner," I said. "How'd you know she was the one?" I had been regularly asking myself that age-old question as my relationship with Stephanie was evolving. I was curious to get the old man's thoughts.

"That's a question so unique to the individual, it can't be answered. But when you know, you just know." *That wasn't very helpful, Mr. X.*

We had completed a small loop around campus and arrived back where we'd first met. We found Cathy there, taking a phone call. She smiled and waved when she saw us.

"How was your walk, boys?" Cathy asked after hanging up. "The campus looks beautiful from what I've seen."

"He had a hard time keeping up," Mr. X said. "He kept asking to borrow my cane. It was sad."

"He's too fast for me," I said. "So we'll see both of you for dinner tonight, right?"

"If you're lucky," Mr. X said. The walk and the sunshine must have put him in a feisty mood.

"Looking forward to it!" Cathy said.

Maybe it was the fresh air or the California sun. Maybe I was excited for them to meet Stephanie. Whatever it was, I was feeling pretty damn good.

CHAPTER 27

Operation Impress-Steph-with-My-Billionaire-Friend was a go. *See, I wasn't lying. I do hang out with the rich and famous, babe.* Plus maybe she'd like Mr. X so much that she'd find my neglecting her for Wichita trips to be a worthy sacrifice.

I made a reservation for four at a nicer Mexican food place. The great thing about Mexican food is you can pick the best place in town and you won't need to sell a kidney if you get stuck paying the bill. Beans, rice, and tortillas can only cost so much. It didn't hurt that we have the home court advantage on Mexican food in California. I was being a good culinary capital allocator.

No surprise, Stephanie looked great. A nice sweater, jeans, fashionable boots, her hair pulled back in a ponytail. I loved how versatile she was. It could be a fancy corporate soiree, a nature hike in the middle of nowhere, or a dressed-down dinner with a billionaire. She had the range to handle it.

We arrived first and were taken to our seats. We chatted about nothing while we waited. I saw Mr. X turn the corner first and scoot along with Cathy in tow. We got up to greet them and received our customary hugs from Cathy.

"How did you land this one?" Mr. X asked me as he shook Stephanie's hand.

"I'm not sure," I said. "Don't remind her." The waitress came around and took our drink orders after we'd settled into our seats.

"So how did you two meet?" Cathy asked.

"She was my drug dealer," I said with no affect. A concerned look spread around the table.

"Caffeine, being the drug," Steph broke in with a mock frown. "I served him his coffee every morning. After months, he finally got up the courage to ask me out," she said. "I thought I was going to have to do it for him."

“Oh, how sweet,” Cathy said. Mr. X added a playful wink.

Stephanie blushed as she smiled and said thank you.

“I hope you don’t mind,” I said. “I took the liberty of ordering us chips and guacamole to start. Have you ever had fresh California guacamole?”

“I don’t believe I have,” said Cathy.

Mr. X just shook his head like he couldn’t care less. “Not my thing,” he said.

“Fun fact, everybody,” I said. “California grows about ninety percent of the nation’s avocados. And this place does it right. You’re in for a treat.”

“What are you studying in school?” Mr. X asked Stephanie. *Sorry to bore you with my guac talk, Gramps.*

“I’m working toward my Ph.D. in social psychology,” she replied. “More specifically, I’m studying decision-making biases and heuristics. I also teach undergraduate psychology classes.”

“Interesting,” Mr. X nodded. “There is no shortage of human folly in this world. You don’t have to look far to find bad decision-making abound.”

“It is quite humbling to study all the different ways we fool ourselves,” she said. “The crazy part is how it happens right under our noses without us knowing. We always assume it only impacts others--that we’re the exception. It must be part of human nature.”

“This may surprise you,” Mr. X said to Stephanie. “But I’ve studied a fair amount of psychology.”

“Really?” she said. “For what?”

“Well, I realized there were some quite useful ideas in there. Ideas that could help with both life and business. If I’ve been successful, it’s because I’ve never been afraid to reach over the fence to grab helpful ideas, no matter the source. I would never have made it in the siloed world of academia."

"You're right," she said. "The incentives in academia are set up to find your little niche and drill deeply, almost to the point of absurdity. The pressure to publish is extreme. It's no wonder you hear stories about data being twisted to support a hypothesis and a crisis of reproducibility."

"Does it seem like your professors get obsessed over one idea?" Mr. X asked. "Like they are a man with a hammer, and every problem in the world looks like a nail?" *He already knew the answer.*

"Yes!" she said. "They identify one useful or interesting phenomenon and then they view the whole world through that one lens. That's how it feels anyway."

"I bet," Mr. X said.

Our server arrived with our chips and the ingredients to make our guacamole. Part of the charm of this restaurant was they made the guacamole right in front of you. The ingredients arrive in small bowls ready to be mixed. With flair, our server added the avocados, salt and pepper, lime juice, minced onions, tomatoes, cilantro, and serrano chiles to a large mortar and ground it with a pestle into a perfect paste.

"You go first, Mr. X," I said.

He wrinkled his nose at the thought as he reached for a chip and dipped it tentatively into the guac. We all watched as he bit off the corner and chewed. He added the rest of the chip to his mouth and continued chewing. His head slowly started to nod. "You know what? That isn't half bad. I'd better have a little more to make sure that first bite wasn't a fluke," he said, reaching for more. We all laughed at his little show. *Mikey likes it!*

I was relieved after all the selling I had done. We all dug in and it wasn't long before we were scraping the bowl clean.

The rest of our meal was filled with great food and laughter. Cathy shared hilarious stories, many of them where Mr. X was the butt of the joke. He took his ribbing good-naturedly. Mr. X shared a few of his own stories, interesting characters he'd met over his decades of business dealings. The check came and Cathy responded like a territorial bulldog when I offered to pay. She wasn't having it, but I at least had to try.

As we walked out, Mr. X seemed to be leaning especially hard on his cane. I got close to help keep him steady. He quietly whispered only to me, "Don't let this one get away, Nick," and nodded toward Stephanie. "She reminds me of my wife. She's a keeper." The little gleam in his eyes took ten years off.

I nodded back. And with that, he stood a little straighter and shuffled his way out of the restaurant with a new vigor. *Keyser Soze.*

CHAPTER 28

Having been able to avoid travel for a few weeks, I felt rejuvenated and excited for my next trip to Wichita. On the plane, I studied the week's Warren Buffett installment, hoping to anticipate the lesson plan. No surprise, I was in the dark.

> -- *"Businesses in industries with both substantial over-capacity and a 'commodity' product are prime candidates for profit troubles. Over-capacity may eventually self-correct, either as capacity shrinks or demand expands. Unfortunately for the participants, such corrections often are long delayed. When they finally occur, the rebound to prosperity frequently produces a pervasive enthusiasm for expansion that, within a few years, again creates over-capacity and a new profitless environment. In other words, nothing fails like success."*
>
> -- *"We do have a few advantages, perhaps the greatest being that we don't have a strategic plan. Thus we feel no need to proceed in an ordained direction (a course leading almost invariably to silly purchase prices) but can instead simply decide what makes sense for our owners. In doing that, we always mentally compare any move we are contemplating with dozens of other opportunities open to us, including the purchase of small pieces of the best businesses in the world via the stock market. Our practice of making this comparison--acquisitions against passive investments--is a discipline that managers focused simply on expansion seldom use."*

My taxi driver gave me a skeptical look when I gave him the address where I was to meet Mr. X. I understood why when we arrived at the empty lot in a rundown part of town. *Was that a clue? Who knows--I was used to showing up dreadfully confused.* Mr. X was already there. I immediately noticed he had upgraded (*downgraded?*) his cane for a walker, one with a built-in seat. I found him sitting patiently with a blanket over his legs. He looked like he'd aged seven years in the few weeks since I'd seen him, but he managed a smile when he saw me approaching.

"Hi, Mr. X," I said.

"Welcome to the future site of a Cootie Burger restaurant," he said with a surprising energy. *Maybe there was still some juice left in him yet?*

I looked around the empty lot and the grey blight that surrounded it. It was a rough part of town. "This is an... *interesting* place for an Cootie Burger, isn't it?" I asked.

"Poor fool," he said with a smile. "You can only see two inches in front of your face."

"What do you mean?" I said.

"Maybe a story will help."

"Lay it on me," I said.

"I was hiking in the woods one day as a much younger man and went through a section of forest where there had been a fire. I couldn't help but notice the only thing growing were pine tree saplings. That got me wondering why these green pine trees were the first thing to make a comeback after a fire. I asked a botanist friend of mine and it turns out conifer trees have evolved a very clever strategy. Do you have any idea what it might be?"

"No clue, Mr. X," I said.

"As you probably know, pine trees release cones that fall to the ground, tumble a bit, and then just sit there. Sometimes for years and years. Big deal, right? But here's where nature gets interesting. Eventually a fire comes along. The flames introduce a new environmental dynamic. The soil becomes richly fertilized by the fire's ashes. Sunlight is suddenly plentiful as trees and brush are burned away. After years of sitting dormant on the forest floor, the patient pine cone springs into action. The heat from the fire opens up the seed pods and releases into the fertile environment where the fledgling pines quickly take hold. Their usual competition has been wiped out--it's a whole new ecological ball game. The pine cones on the forest floor wait to take advantage of the eventual disruption, and it's proven a very effective survival strategy. But it requires extreme patience," he said. *I'll admit, I was mesmerized whenever he'd spool up into teaching mode like this.*

"I'll probably never look at a pine cone the same way," I said. " But I still don't see how this relates to an empty lot in a rundown part of town?"

"Imagine being patient like the pine cone," he said, "waiting... ready to take advantage of disruptions in the system. Change is unavoidable, but we can use it to our advantage. One strategy that's been successful for us at Cootie has been buying plots of land in areas of urban blight where we believe there's a good chance of revitalization. Everything moves in cycles: growth, eventual decay, cleansing tear down, repeat. The forest and the city aren't so different. When an area is particularly rough, we're able to acquire properties for very low prices. The buildings and services like water and electricity are often still in decent shape."

"Really?" I said.

"The low price today makes sense," he replied. "Who wants to buy in this shabby state? You couldn't get much cash flow from this property as it exists right now. So there's not much to support the asset's price. But that's very short-sighted in my view."

"So you're saying that someday this will be a nice part of town?" I looked around and tried to imagine new buildings, new families moving in, and new energy injected into the area. *Maybe it's possible.* "I guess it's not that hard to picture. Anything would be an improvement, right?" I said.

"Here's the hard part of the strategy," he said. "We have to wait. And wait. And wait. In some cases, it's taken over ten years of just sitting on the property doing nothing but paying property taxes. When most CEOs are measured by the quarter, it's very difficult to be that patient. The wheels of progress turn imperceptibly slowly. But eventually a rough neighborhood gets cleaned up. We then have a location in a hot area, and we paid a favorable price for the real estate. Now we have a material advantage over our competitors for a long stretch. Just like the pine cone, we have a head start after the fire."

"My grandfather always used to tell me to buy sweaters in the summer," I recalled. "Is this along the same lines?"

"It's similar," he said. "But in this case the seasons run longer than most can tolerate. Especially if they have investors who require immediate returns. It can really cloud a decision-maker's thinking when there's a shot clock."

"I can see how it'd be difficult to have patience in the typical corporate environment. At Big Rock, they're always looking to turn things around as fast as possible and then sell before the wheels fall off."

"That's one way to do business. It doesn't fit with my personality. Here's the lesson I want you to take away from the humble pine cone. Patience may be the least-exploited advantage in the game. While we're talking about strategy and patience, I have another story for you."

"I love your stories," I said. *I wasn't buttering him up; I actually did love his stories.*

"Do you remember much of the 1980s?" he asked.

"A little bit. Like *Back to the Future* or *Miami Vice*?"

"I meant more in the business world," he said.

"Not really. I have seen the movie *Wall Street*."

"Close enough," he said with a shrug. "That movie gives you a sense of the feeling of greed that permeated the culture. Around that time, it became very easy to borrow money, even if you were a little dodgy on how you would pay it back. The idea was you could always borrow more and reset the clock when the debt was due. No problem, as long as the money was flowing."

"I think I remember reading about that," I said.

"The money companies borrowed came when they issued what were called 'junk bonds.' Now they're called 'high yield bonds,' so they must be quite a bit better than back then," Mr. X said sarcastically. *Nice euphemism, Wall Street.* "We were coming out of the 1970s which were a very turbulent time in the U.S. Inflation, Vietnam, long gas lines."

"Disco!" I cut in.

"Yes, even disco," he said. "As the 1980s got rolling, a fresh sense of optimism was in the air. And naturally, access to cheap money made people's eyes bigger than their checkbooks. They were overconfident about the kind of businesses they could build. In my industry, there were several restaurant chains who borrowed a lot of money and built new stores. Lots of stores. They saw a bright future ahead."

"I assume from your tone that you weren't building like they were. What did you see?"

"You're right, we weren't building anything. Our competitors had bid up the price of land, raw materials, and construction labor to the point where new buildings were very expensive and it was hard to see how we'd make our money back. I've noticed that when there's a lot of easy money sloshing around, the returns on capital start to suffer. Instead of borrowing, we ended up accumulating a lot of cash through operations and just sitting on it. The press at the time said we were behind the times, indecisive, old and stodgy. That we were going to be left in the dust by all of these movers and shakers. And I was a much younger man back then!"

"I bet that was hard to listen to," I said.

"I wouldn't be much of a rebel if I let it bother me, would I?" he said. "Besides, what was the alternative? Do something that didn't make sense, just to be like everyone else? That would be patently foolish."

"You've earned your 'rebel' moniker," I teased. "So what happened?"

"Unfortunately for the aggressive ones, economies are cyclical, much like nature. Trees don't grow to the sky in nature or business. There are feedback mechanisms which create cycles, limits, and reversions to the mean. And just like nature, these cycles take years to play out. It's very difficult to watch from the sidelines for years--to wait patiently while your pine cones just sit on the forest floor."

"With the price of everything going up, did it seem like everyone was making easy money but you? I vaguely remember stories from the dot com mania that everyone was getting stupid rich overnight."

"Yes, it had many of the same hallmarks. As I said, these companies borrowed a lot of money to build new stores. They got ahead of themselves with how much restaurant space consumers really wanted. It's simple economics: any time you have too much supply, prices start dropping. All the projections on how they were going to pay back that debt went sour because they couldn't get the prices they needed due to overcapacity. Boom is followed by bust, surely as night follows day. Many of these companies went into bankruptcy or were taken over by competitors at very cheap prices. Who wants money-losing assets after all?" His tone had a hint that he was leaving me a clue. His pregnant silence confirmed my suspicion.

"Wait, weren't they making money?" I said. "Just not as much as people originally thought they would when they borrowed to build?"

"That's right!" he said. "That's an important takeaway of this story. There's really no such thing as a *bad asset*. Just paying the wrong price for that asset."

"After being proved right, I bet it felt good to tell everyone, 'I told you so!'" I said.

"No, you should know me well enough to know that's not my style," he gently scolded. "We quietly went on a buying spree. We used our pile of cash to purchase dozens of great buildings out of bankruptcy for twenty-five cents on the dollar. Reminder me later to tell you a story about Conrad Hilton."

"OK."

"We also acquired an entire private burger chain and absorbed them into Cootie. We even bought the stock of a tough competitor we felt was unduly cheap in the stock market. It was a very productive time, all set up by our patience during the boom period. Both the private acquisition and stock purchase are longer stories for a different time."

"Didn't you have the same problem of weak pricing that fouled up everyone else?"

"We did," he said. "For a while. But eventually the economy grew to where we had the *right* number of restaurants. I say *right* with tongue-in-cheek. There's no right number, at least not one that any human could calculate. Just like there's no *right* number of trees in the forest. Humans wouldn't be able to figure out what that is either. The number and type of restaurants people want is an ever-changing calculus based on the desires and needs of our tastes. And that's just for restaurants! It's sheer lunacy to think you could plan an entire economy. No wonder the Soviet Union collapsed." I had yet to read anything about economic miscalculation being the cause of the collapse of communism. I had always been told it was because they didn't fully commit to true socialism. "Sorry… where was I before I went off on a tangent?"

"I was asking about soft pricing," I said, getting us back on track.

"Ah, yes," he said. "Anyway, as demand caught up with supply, prices firmed up, even overshooting when there became a shortage. Always in cycles. Remember back to when we talked about the importance of same-store-sales to profitability?"

"Yes," I said. "Operational leverage."

"Good boy. As we had more people coming through the same four walls to buy burgers, we earned an increasingly higher margin on each burger. As traffic increased, we enjoyed that tailwind at our sails."

"So would it be fair to say that you zigged when everyone else was zagging?" I asked.

"Sort of. We weren't being contrary for no reason though. Their zagging just made no sense to me. There's an ebb and flow that's woven into the very fabric of capitalism. People who forget cyclicality are bound to be hurt by the bust, whereas we were able to benefit. Every bubble forces you to make a choice: do you want to look like a fool during the build up as you're missing out? Or would you rather look like a fool after it bursts? There's no getting around looking foolish. But you do get to decide the time frame. I call it 'The Bubble Ultimatum.'"

"I think I now understand the quote you sent about over-capacity and under-capacity causing price swings and cycles. 'Nothing fails like success.' And you might add, 'Nothing succeeds like failure,' right?" He just nodded. *Not even a high-five for my cleverness?*

"Now, I have a quiz for you," he said.

"Uh oh..."

"You'll be fine. We're now standing in an empty lot. To sell hamburgers, we need to have a building here eventually. We have to put a roof over our head to provide the restaurant experience people are accustomed to. Here's the quiz question: how many different options does Cootie have to create a roof over our customer's heads?" *This must be a trick question.*

"I can only think of one option. Hiring a construction crew to erect a building for you. Is that what you mean? What else is there?"

"Where's the creative thinking these days?" he muttered. "I can think of at least eight ways."

"Eight?!" I said. *How is that even possible?*

"At least. Let's start with the most obvious. We could buy a fresh plot of land like this one and build on it immediately. That's one option, as you mentioned. We could buy land by itself and wait to eventually put a building on it. That would be a second option. We could technically buy a building and store it somewhere before we have the land, like a manufactured home. We haven't tried that one yet, by the way. That makes three options to start. What else?" he said.

"I see how this works," I said. "You're being tricky. Let's see… you could buy an existing building and convert it to a Cootie Burger."

"Good," he said. "Have you ever heard of Conrad Hilton?"

"I've heard of Paris Hilton... 'That's hot.'" *He didn't get my joke.*

"I think she's his great-granddaughter. Conrad created Hilton Hotels. He was a builder who was almost wiped out by the Great Depression. He saw how cheap hotels could get in times of panic compared to what they cost him to build and he came to a realization. From that moment forward, he'd only buy distressed properties and would never build anything himself again. For the rest of his life he'd only wait for property to go on sale. Anyway, that's four," he said encouragingly. "Keep going."

"You could buy a competitor's chain and convert all of its restaurants into Cootie Burgers?" I said.

"Very good, although I basically gave you that one with the Hilton story. That's five."

"I'm not sure what the other three are," I finally said.

"You're going to think this is cheating, but see if you can follow. We could calculate how much a publicly-traded competitor is selling for on a per-restaurant basis and buy partial ownership by investing in their stock. You'd have less control than if you built a Cootie Burger yourself, but it's still a way to become the owner of a roof for a restaurant operation."

"That is sneaky," I said. "But I can see how if you were able to get a good deal on a competitor by buying their stock, it might make more sense than building your own new store to compete with them. Especially if you're worried about creating overcapacity and harming the industry's pricing."

"Exactly right. Mr. Buffett would be proud of that observation." *The old man got me with that one. I tingled with pride.* "So that makes six ways, leaving us with at least two more."

My silence indicated I was stumped.

"OK," he said patiently. "This one applies if you're a publicly traded company and can be a little hard to conceptualize at first. You can buy back your own stock, which in a way is purchasing some of your own roofs back from your business partners. That'd be seven."

"Sorry, I didn't follow that one."

"That's alright. We'll discuss stock buybacks more at a later time. They're a very important topic and I don't want to give them short shrift. Here's a hint for the last one: deciding not to decide is still a decision."

Exasperated, I laughed, "Mr. X, your hints are never helpful."

"Just think about it for a minute," he said.

"Are you counting not doing anything and just keeping cash in your bank account an option?"

"Indeed, I am. Remember our patient pinecone sitting on the forest floor? Often the smartest thing to do is nothing. Wait for a better slate of opportunities to be presented on your menu."

"Jeez, eight ways just to put a roof over your head," I said. "Even a simple business like running a restaurant sure seems complicated. Capital allocation is hard."

"Perhaps, but it's not so bad once you have the menu laid out in front of you. All you have to do is evaluate each idea and decide on the most logical choice. This is the secret to good capital allocation. Have a lot of options and pick the best one. You want to cast the net wide when you're measuring all of your choices against each other. It's the missed opportunities right in front of your face that really hurt."

"The ones that got away..." I said. *I should have been a philosopher.*

"You have no idea how true that is," he replied in a haunting tone.

"I think I understand the other quote now and why Mr. Buffett doesn't stress about not having a long term plan," I said.

"Oh yeah, why is that?" Mr. X replied.

"At every juncture, he's looking at his various investment options and trying to pick the smartest one. Even if the answer is to wait for a better menu. How can you make too many plans if you don't know what opportunities the future holds? You're limiting yourself by pre-deciding today what the best option is ten years from now."

"That's the smartest thing I've heard you say," he said.

"Must be picking up some good habits from hanging around the right people."

"Must be."

"Mr. X, do you think of yourself as happy?" I asked.

"That's quite the segue," he said. "To tell you the truth, I haven't spent a lot of time thinking about my own happiness. I've always felt my best when I've focused on being useful to others. And the most useful version of myself has always been in the business world."

"Do you think those feelings of wanting to be useful come from your upbringing?"

"Probably," he said. "You couldn't worry about concepts like being happy when you're living on the edge. Even after my life had become materially more comfortable, I always felt the urge to keep striving. Like maybe the other shoe would drop if I relaxed too much."

"Sounds exhausting," I said.

"It is. But when it's all you've ever known, it feels normal."

"There's something that's been bothering me for a while," I said.

"What is it, Nick?" he said.

"Why did you pick me?" I asked. "It just doesn't make any sense. You could have gotten anyone you wanted to write about you."

"You're right," he said. "I've been approached by many to write a biography and I've turned them all down. Part of it is that my own mortality stares me in the face every day. I can see life draining out. It feels like now or never."

"But why *me*?" Mr. X stared me in the eyes as if he were contemplating an important decision.

"You didn't know it at the time, but your first visit to Wichita with your classmates was a job interview," he said. "I have research done on every member of an audience I'm going to speak to. It helps me choose where to steer the conversation to make the biggest impact."

"Are you serious?" I said.

"If I'm going to do something, I'm going to do it to the best of my damned abilities," he said. "There's no excuse for poor preparation." *Wow, what did my dossier look like?*

"You caught my eye for a few reasons," he continued. "First, you had a background in both business and journalism. Having a pure biography written isn't of much interest to me. Who cares about a poor farm boy from Kansas? I want this book to be something others can learn from to make them better businesspeople."

"Little did you know how dumb I was about business," I said.

"It took a little hand-holding at the beginning, but you've blossomed into an apt pupil, Nick."

"Thanks, Mr. X," I said.

"Your working at Big Rock was also a factor," he said. "I knew you'd be seeing a version of capitalism that is pretty far from what I espouse. My hope was that you'd be able to appreciate the differences. Maybe you'd be able to wrestle the term away from Big Rock's version that I think gives capitalism a bad name."

"I'd have to be pretty blind not to see the difference between you and Big Rock."

"It also didn't take a Sherlock Holmes to find your columns in the school paper and figure out that you were strongly anti-capitalist." I didn't know what to say to that before he continued, "I wanted someone who would be critical of my views. If I was able to make a believer out of you, then I knew the project could help anyone."

"I have to be honest; you've challenged many of my core beliefs," I said.

"I suspected that might happen," he said. "It was also important to me that you were young. I've noticed a disturbing trend toward socialism in today's youth. I'm less concerned with my generation appreciating capitalism--they'll be gone soon enough. It's the next generation of decision-makers I want to influence. I'm an old man; there was no chance I'd be able to connect with your generation. But I thought you might be an ideal translator to reach them."

"I've always felt like an outcast with people my age, but I see your point," I said.

"An outcast... or a rebel?" he said with a pointed tone.

"I'm working my way up to rebel."

"The last piece of the puzzle fell into place on your first visit to Wichita. I wanted to get a first hand sense what you were made of. You weren't afraid to think for yourself and stand up to me about taking notes, and you asked a great question under pressure. I was testing you." My head was spinning with realizations.

"I have a confession, Mr. X," I said quietly. "I'm embarrassed to tell you this, but my original plan with accepting this project was to dig up dirt on you. I wanted to write a takedown series about you and the evils of capitalism."

"I thought that might be the case," he said. "But I had a good feeling I'd win you over, and there isn't much dirt for you to dig up. I've always lived my life as if anything I did would be shared on the front page of the newspaper with everyone I cared about."

What... the... eff? This whole time I thought I was working my way into Mr. X's good graces to write the ultimate business takedown piece. Yet all along I was the one being played. He was playing chess, I was playing checkers. I would have thought that I'd feel angry, but I was strangely relieved. Like I had been meandering along the edge of a cliff and Mr. X had pulled me back just before plunging over.

"I'm sorry that I accepted this assignment under false pretenses, Mr. X," I said with as much humility as I could muster. "Can you ever forgive me?"

"Of course, Nick," he said. "And I'm sorry if you felt like I was playing puppet master. But I knew all along that you'd come out of this with new perspectives and hopefully glad you were selected."

"You have no idea how thankful I am," I said.

"That's probably enough for today," he said. "It's too cold out here for an old man. I'll see you in a few weeks."

"Thank you, Mr. X," I said. It was cold outside, yet inside I felt the warm glow of genuine appreciation for my elderly mentor. *Maybe even love?*

CHAPTER 29

It had been six months since my first date with Stephanie. I was so busy spinning plates I almost missed the milestone. I planned a nice dinner and bought her a pair of zirconium diamond earrings with literally all of the money I had in my bank account. *No more credit cards for this guy!* My humble offering was vital to laying the groundwork for a major ask: I wanted to move in together.

I had never breached this relationship Maginot Line. *This was real adult relationship stuff. Way over my head.* I was sure she was going to think I was crazy. Maybe even break up with me for asking so soon.

At dinner, after the presentation of the earrings, I screwed up my courage. Being a natural romantic, I lead with the idea that we'd save money by moving in together. We'd only pay one rent, share the utilities, our food bills likely reduced. It made sense economically. *Every girl's fairytale.*

She hesitated; my pitch was going off the rails. *Time for a Hail Mary.* I said, "And besides all that, I just like spending time with you and this will give us a chance to share those little moments between life's happening that make it magical. I know it seems kinda quick, but when you know, you just know." *Thanks for the assist, Mr. X.* She lit up like a Christmas tree.

"You're right," she said. "We should move in together. My lease is up pretty soon and I was considering moving anyway. And like you said, we'll both be able to save more money. Let's do it." She beamed; I just stared. I wanted to sear this memory into my consciousness forever. Making her happy swelled my heart.

After a diligent search, we found an apartment. It was slightly nicer than either of the studio apartment hovels we were currently inhabiting. It had two tiny bedrooms--*fancy times!* The only downside was it was located near the light-rail tracks.

As in, *right below* the tracks. We got to know the light-rail schedule intimately, but you get used to the noise faster than you might expect. Some odd part of you even starts to crave it. It didn't take long for it to feel like home.

We weren't far from the light-rail stop, which meant we had an easy jump off point to adventure around the city. The local baseball team had cheap tickets and even cheaper hot dogs on Tuesday nights. I didn't have class that evening, so game night quickly became our weekly ritual. Light-rail home meant we could drink all the beer we wanted, or until my wallet was empty, usually the latter. The team had a young batch of rising stars who were delivering ahead of schedule. The future held so much promise.

This isn't a fairytale. My own insecurities started rearing their ugly heads. *You probably knew they would eventually. Why was she so friendly with that good-looking guy in her lab? Who is she texting with?* Everyone has their own brand of crazy that they can mostly hide from the rest of the world. But when you live with someone, eventually the armor cracks. Cohabitation is a whole different ball of wax from dating. It's hard not to lose a little of the magic when you peek behind the curtain. There are so many small opportunities to pick at the edges of the relationship, loosening the threads.

Inevitably both Steph and I started to let our demons out, and it wasn't always pretty. Our good times together were amazing. I'd never been in a relationship where I cared this much. But our bad times raised real doubts, at least inside my noisy head.

> *Didn't you say you were going to vacuum while I was gone?*
> *The clothes are clean in the basket--just put them away!*
> *Am I the only one who ever cleans out the fridge?*
> *Gross, don't leave your hair in the sink.*

It's fine. (Definitely not fine.)

Her most biting remarks were around how busy I always was. To be fair, I had a lot going on between work, school, and Wichita. When any unexpected deadline would come up, my time with Steph was the shock absorber to take the hit. I could tell she was feeling neglected.

It was a confusing time for me. Mr. X was chipping the scales from my eyes every few weeks. I didn't know what I wanted to be when I grew up anymore. When we'd visit Steph's parents for dinner, I could feel her dad shooting icy daggers my way. He didn't like me; my hunch was he thought his daughter could do better. *He might have been right.*

I was pretty sure Stephanie was special. I knew I was usually a better version of myself around her. But it was my first serious relationship. Where was the third-party independent assessment to tell us we were a good match? I wondered if I had time for a serious relationship. I wondered if we were too young and things had progressed too far, too fast. Like somehow *the relationship* had taken on a life and momentum of its own, independent of either of us. I felt swept along in it. *Like I said, I was confused.*

I'd ask myself everyday: had I met the right girl, but maybe just at the wrong time?

CHAPTER 30

Cathy called to tell me that Mr. X was not doing well and he might need to cancel my next trip out. At the last minute, she said I should come out just in case. Perhaps reflecting Mr. X's fading vitality, this week's quote was short.

"Start with the customer and work backwards."
- Jeff Bezos

Cathy set it up for me to meet Mr. X near the riverwalk in downtown Wichita. His doctors had advised him to get more outdoor fresh air. Seeing him appear with the walker last time had been jarring, but this time was much worse. Cathy appeared pushing Mr. X in a wheelchair. His hair was a messy thicket, and not just from the continual light breeze that was blowing. He looked like he might have just woken up.

"Nice wheels," I said.

"At least I can still sit up," he shot back with an unexpected vigor. His mind was still sharp, imprisoned in the crumbling architecture of his body. *Ugh, what an awful thing to happen to someone.*

"OK, boys," Cathy said. "I'm going to take advantage of this time downtown to do some shopping. Do you think you can handle this thing?"

"The old man or the wheelchair?" I said.

"You're lucky I can't stand up, sonny."

"Call me if you need anything," Cathy said over her shoulder as she beelined for a dose of retail therapy.

Mr. X and I walked for a while, reconnecting with small talk. He asked how Stephanie was doing. Good, I said. *When I was around to see her.* I asked for the latest on his medical conditions. He didn't share a lot of details except to say that it was getting worse. *Ya think?* We walked passed a giant art installation, a statue of a Native American in full headdress. He was wielding a tomahawk in both hands, about to land a blow that would never fall. Behind the statue in the near distance were thick black threads attached to aluminum towers carrying high voltage electricity. I marvelled at the juxtaposition between the old and new symbols of power.

"Did you like the Jeff Bezos quote?" Mr. X said. *Schools in.*

"I liked that it was short," I said.

"Figures," he said. "Let's unpack what he's saying. I'll start by giving you a thought experiment that can be applied to any business. At Cootie, we call it the Eleven-Star Experience Exercise. Kind of a mouthful, but the name doesn't matter."

"I thought you could only go up to five stars?"

Before he could reply, he shook violently in a fit of coughing. He settled down and continued, "I think that's true, but you'll see why we have eleven. Have you ever stayed at a five-star hotel?"

"No, I'm not a billionaire, remember," I said. "But I've seen enough movies to have a pretty good idea what it might be like."

"This shouldn't surprise you, but I hardly ever stay at fancy hotels. I feel out of place and just don't need that kind of luxury... my poor Kansas roots, I guess?"

"Anything better than dirt floors and an outhouse would be an upgrade," I said.

"Back to our thought experiment. What would you expect a six-star experience to be like?" he said.

I thought for a moment, "Well, I'd want my own private butler, that's for sure." I pictured myself as Lloyd Christmas from Dumb and Dumber handing out wads of cash to attentive servants. "*There you go... there you go...*"

Mr. X snapped me out of my daydream, "How about a seven-star experience?"

"Let's see, they'd know all of my favorite foods. And the TV would only show the channels I liked."

We continued the conversation like this through three more stars of increasing ridiculousness. Eventually, Mr. X asked, "Finally, what would an eleven-star experience look like?"

"For me, it'd be on the moon. There'd be an elaborate production where I was James Bond and we'd re-enact *Moonraker*. And just like Bond, I'd defeat the bad guy and get the girl." Mr. X smiled at the ludicrous idea of my perfect experience.

"So other than some fun daydreaming, what is the point of this thought exercise?" he asked rhetorically. "Obviously a hotel couldn't afford to send you to the moon and make you James Bond for any reasonable price. But if we can anchor our mindsets upward to an eleven-star experience, it really opens up what might be feasible and innovative at a lower level to make the customer feel fantastic. Every business will be different. It's about cracking our minds open to find the obvious improvements that are hiding in plain sight."

"Interesting," I said. "If you go ridiculously far in one direction, other ideas don't seem so crazy. You change the reference point."

I pushed the wheelchair along the river walk. We were both quiet with our thoughts. Something occurred to me. "Mr. X," I said. "If you're trying to deliver maximum value to Cootie Burger customers, shouldn't you offer more than just burgers, fries, and shakes? What about someone who wants a chicken sandwich? Or a salad? If you gave customers more choices, they could pick what they wanted and would maximize their subjective experience. They could shift their own *Value* straws out farther if they got to pick, right?"

He smiled, presumably at my reference to his straws. "That's a very logical observation, Nick. In fact, it was an idea my father fell victim to. While I was away at college, he experimented with all kinds of different menu options. Fried chicken, grits and okra--you name it. It seemed like a good idea, but it nearly destroyed the business. I had to learn the hard way why it didn't work."

"What happened?" I asked.

"The problem is, humans aren't always logical. Our brains evolved for survival, not necessarily logic. Have you ever heard of the paradox of choice?" he asked.

"No."

"It's a simple enough concept. As you give people more choices, it gets harder for them to make a decision. They start to feel overwhelmed."

"I've had that feeling before at the freezer aisle trying to decide which ice cream to buy."

"Me, too," he said. "People end up less happy with their final choice because it seems like they gave up too many other great options to choose just one."

"Damn you, Cherry Garcia. I knew I should have picked Rocky Road!" I said.

His chuckle devolved into a coughing fit. I felt bad for instigating the attack. "The grass is always greener," he eventually said. "Especially in today's modern society when we have so many options. We're bombarded with constant decisions. One study found that the average adult makes thirty thousand decisions per day. We end up making bad choices on the big stuff because we've drained all our decision-making energy on the inconsequential."

"I might have read about that before," I said. "Apparently Steve Jobs wore the same black turtleneck all of the time for that reason. He didn't have to waste any effort picking out what to wear from his closet."

"I do something similar, but it's not as extreme. Mostly hospital gowns these days," he lamented.

"So back to my original question, Mr. X. Why doesn't Cootie have a bigger menu? Too many choices make people unhappy?"

"We're doing our customers a favor," he said. "We're making their choices more manageable. There are some good business reasons to have a simplified menu. It makes managing inventory much easier. You don't have to throw away spoiling food because people didn't want chicken sandwiches that week for some reason. Throwing away food in the restaurant business is akin to throwing away money."

"Hard to make a profit when you're throwing money into the garbage," I said.

"For sure. It also simplifies your operations. You don't have to train employees on how to make ten different items. They make fewer mistakes, and new hires get up to speed faster. It's not that big of a deal when we're talking about making hamburgers, but for other businesses, it can make a real difference."

"And maybe most importantly," he continued. "There's a glitch in the human mind: if you offer only one or two things, people assume you do those few things very well. Maybe even the best. If you took your car in for an oil change and the auto shop also did hair cuts, would you expect them to be very good at either service?"

"Probably not. Though if you wanted one of those greaser haircuts from the 1950s, that'd be the place to go."

"Maybe that's an unexplored niche?" he joked. "The important point is people can only remember so many things about your business. They're busy living their lives. You want to make it easy and unambiguous for them to form associations about what you're good at."

"I think one of my professors called that a *unique selling proposition*. Is that right?"

"Yes," he said. "Could your customers explain in ten seconds what makes you so great? We do burgers, fries, and shakes at Cootie. Full stop. We happen to focus on quality and provide great service. Because we don't offer anything else, it's very clear what you're going to get when you visit. People know what to expect, which is comforting. So when one of their friends asks where's a great place to get a burger, we own that space in their mind and they reflexively think of us. That becomes a form of advertising."

"Oh, due to the brand that you've built through so many customer interactions," I said, connecting dots with our past conversations. "That *fat* that you have stored in your customers' minds."

"That's exactly why over-delivering on value is such an important goal for us," he said. "Someone sharing the best place to get a burger with a friend is worth how many TV or radio advertising spots? Can you name the brand of the last radio commercial you heard?"

"Umm… no," I said.

"How about the last great restaurant someone told you to check out?"

I thought for a second, "Yes, a little hole-in-the-wall taqueria near campus. They have amazing salsa."

"You get my point," he said. "Let's think a little more broadly. One of the most important expenses any business has is the cost to find customers and get them in the door. In business school, they probably called it 'customer acquisition cost.'"

"That sounds familiar," I said.

"It's simple enough. Cootie could invest in radio advertising to get people to come eat our burgers. We could advertise on billboards. Or skywriting. Or on the internet. Each medium has a certain cost and expected return in traffic, though it's usually very difficult to measure that return. There's an old joke in advertising that fifty percent of ads are massively successful and fifty percent of ads are a total waste." He paused to build for the punchline. "The problem is, no one knows which half is which!" With this he laughed heartily and spiraled himself into another coughing fit. *At least it wasn't my fault this time.*

"I didn't know there were advertising-specific jokes," I said.

"There are," he nodded. "I have another one for you in a minute. I want to make something clear first: there's nothing wrong with traditional advertising. We use it at Cootie. We just happen to believe focusing on a stellar in-store experience and viral word-of-mouth are more effective for us. What's really nice is that if a customer refers us to a friend, they're basically making a public proclamation that they like eating at our restaurant. People have a strong internal desire to appear consistent with what they say to their friends. So by making the referral, they reinforce their own good feelings and commitment to liking Cootie."

"Are you saying when a customer refers a friend, they're almost referring themselves all over again?" I asked.

"You said it better than I did… first time for everything," he said. "Here's that other advertising joke I promised. It's more of a pithy observation. When you stop to think about it, a flower is nothing more than a weed with an advertising budget."

"Huh, I guess that's true," I said. "Humans go to great lengths to plant flowers. But we pull weeds out of the ground because we don't like their *advertising*. But is there really much of a difference? They're both just plants trying to survive and propagate."

"There's a very profound idea buried in that joke," he said. "Remember back to our Iron Rule of Economic Survival. What does successful advertising do to our triangles?"

"There's obviously a cost involved. You have to buy ad space or pay the skywriting pilot," I said.

"True," he nodded. "Keep going--think of a great ad you saw. How did it make you feel inside?"

After a bit of reminiscing, I said, "I remember when I was a kid the Gatorade commercials with Michael Jordan. I was never that into sports, but my best friend loved watching him play basketball. He used to say that drinking Gatorade was his chance to 'Be Like Mike.' He told me he was drinking the same lemon-lime flavor that Jordan drank during his games."

"That's a great example," he said. "So Gatorade was able to take yellow-colored sugar water and make him feel he could be Michael Jordan. How much more do you think he enjoyed Gatorade because of that commercial?"

"He told me he made sure to have it at every game, as part of a good luck routine," I said. "I was never like Mike. I was a foot shorter than everyone else and could barely dribble."

"I'm sure you brought other skills?" he said in a fatherly way.

"Yeah, I kept the bench warm for all the other players."

"Every experience makes us who we are," he said tenderly. "Back to our lesson. Advertising has two functions: make people aware of the product, and shift out that *V* straw and increase the perceived value a customer experiences. If you can nudge *V* out farther than the cost required, I'd consider that to be a sound strategic expense. At Cootie we happen to focus on quality ingredients and a great customer experience, but that doesn't mean it's the only way. Gatorade dramatically increased the perceived value of their drinks in your friend's mind through their association with Michael Jordan."

"I guess there are a lot more ways to shift the *Value* straw than I realized," I said.

"Indeed, and if your business focuses on discovering and expanding on those ways through imagining Eleven-Star Experiences, you have a good shot at making your customers feel great--which is the whole point of business." *Ugh, there was that feeling of discomfort again in the pit of my chest. I was definitely warming up to the whole concept of business when it was explained by my Midwest Miyagi. It seemed unthinkable: the idea that capitalism actually served the little people instead of taking advantage of them? Che would not approve. Talk about cognitive dissonance.*

Mr. X sat quietly while I pushed him along in his chair. He instructed me to turn onto a small paved path that lead away from the river. We went over a few small hills and came to the gate of a cemetery. Mr. X said to go inside. *OK...*

We wound our way through the grey and black headstones that popped from the verdant grass. Life and death in stark relief. I did the math on how long the deceased had lived as we meandered by the headstones. I tried to imagine what their lives had been like based on the dates. All those thoughts, hopes, and dreams that make up a person, distilled to a slab of rock with some etchings on it. *Dust in the wind...*

Mr. X navigated via monosyllabic instructions as we walked deeper into the graveyard. "I want to tell you a very personal story." *Have I finally broken through to him?*

"OK, Mr. X," I said. He was staring off into the distance as we glided along the weaving path.

"I mentioned before that I have…" he paused as the words stuck in his throat. "... *had* an amazing wife and daughter. I also had a son. His name was Edward, but we called him Eddie. He was a special kid. Smart, precocious, though a bit of a showoff. When Eddie was nine years old, he came down with a cough. Nothing out of the ordinary for a healthy kid, but after awhile, it wouldn't go away."

Mr. X pointed to an offshoot of the main path and we followed a capillary into a section of headstones. He held up his hand, signaling to stop. I followed his eyes to a smaller stone with a handsome placard. Reading it grabbed my soul with a wrench.

Edward Richard Xavier
1961-1971

"We took Eddie in to see the doctor. After a battery of tests, we discovered he had a tumor in his chest cavity. The doctor scheduled a surgery to remove it..." He trailed off, staring out at the rolling hills. The thick blanket of clouds fit the somber mood. "We knew the surgery carried risks..." His eyes were moist, the wound torn open again for probably the millionth time. His voice was gravel, "Eddie didn't survive the surgery."

"I'm sorry, Mr. X," I whispered and squeezed his shoulder.

"I remember wandering the streets of Wichita, lost, alone with my grief, crying uncontrollably. My wife and daughter were at home, but I just couldn't bear seeing them at that point. I stumbled down the street saying Eddie's name over and over again out loud as my mind played highlights of our short time with him." Tears were now streaming down his crinkled face. "Even more painful was imagining the moments that would never come to be. I'm sure I looked like a lunatic..." He took time to recompose himself.

"Don't forget," he said. "You never know the fight someone else is struggling with. You don't know their circumstances, so be careful with your judgments. To people going about their lives in Wichita in 1971, I looked like I should be in an asylum."

"I can only imagine..." I said. I was having trouble finding any words. *Poor Mr. X.*

"The other point of this story is that life can be damned unfair. I've never gotten over losing Eddie. And I never will. That's all I have to say right now. Please take me back."

The old man had dealt with a lot in his life. Maybe everyone who reaches a certain age has their portion of sad stories. I'd later learn that I didn't know the half of Mr. X's.

CHAPTER 31

It was time for my midterm presentation on Zero-Based Budgeting (ZBB) for my Budgets and Controls class. It served as a nice dress rehearsal for my pitch at Big Rock. I had been practicing for weeks in a vain attempt to overcome my shoddy public-speaking skills.

I was nervous before I started my talk at school. Glancing around the room, I realized that my indifferent classmates were busy surfing the web and couldn't have cared less about what I was saying. That made it a little easier. I focused on my professor and ran through my presentation as if we were the only two in the room. It went off without a hitch and I got a good grade. *Yeah!* I felt ready for my big chance at Big Rock later that week.

"Cost is the variable that managers have the most control over in a business," I began to a room full of Big Rock bigwigs. *Not exactly, "It was the best of times, it was the worst of times," but how exciting can budgeting be?*

I explained the basics of ZBB. The analysis of *strategic* versus *non-strategic* costs, determined by the delight of customers. The problem of hoarding resources and use-it-or-lose-it budget inertia. You couldn't just spend the same amount as last year. The burden of proof was to justify every expense. If it wasn't an effective use of capital, then it had to go.

I wanted to give the higher-ups something more tangible. I explained the studies which found that when properly implemented, ZBB could reduce costs by ten to twenty percent, often within six months. I picked out a specific company that Big Rock had recently acquired and showed them projections of a fifteen percent savings in the operating budget within four months of the adoption of ZBB.

I explained that ZBB was a way to cut out bogus spending and make resources available for the most-promising strategies. If a company reinvests in profitable growth, it will eventually show up as increased earnings, available for more intelligent reinvestment. Your goal is a compounding of business value in a virtuous cycle. I sprinkled in liberal doses of Mr. X's favorite Warren Buffett quotes.

As I wrapped up, a lively conversation broke out among the upper brass at Big Rock. They had apparently only heard half my presentation. Specifically, the half about cutting costs. This was the academic equivalent of telling the wolf it was OK to enter the henhouse. ZBB would be the cover for them to squeeze budgets as close to zero as possible and cut everything to the bone.

They missed the second half of my message about reinvesting back into strategic expenses to delight customers. Cutting *non-strategic* fat in order to build *strategic* muscle. Reinvestment and the compounding of value creation that propels humanity forward.

It was bittersweet when management later announced I had won the competition and the trip for two to Catalina Island. *A pyrrhic victory if there ever was one.* I learned a stark lesson in how hard it is to create change in a big organization.

CHAPTER 32

I couldn't wait to tell Mr. X about my win and the Catalina trip. The next visit to Wichita rolled around and I received my customary note.

> *"I made an even worse mistake when I said 'yes' to Dexter, a shoe business I bought in 1993 for $433 million in Berkshire stock (25,203 shares of A). What I had assessed as durable competitive advantage vanished within a few years. But that's just the beginning: By using Berkshire stock, I compounded this error hugely. That move made the cost to Berkshire shareholders not $400 million, but rather $3.5 billion. In essence, I gave away 1.6% of a wonderful business – one now valued at $220 billion – to buy a worthless business."*
>
> \- Warren Buffett

Cathy had instructed me to wait at curbside pickup at the airport. Mr. X would be fetching me in a town car. *Look at me now.* When the sleek black car pulled up, a driver I didn't recognize hopped out and opened the rear door for me. Mr. X was waiting in the back seat. He looked frail, almost childlike from the weight he'd been shedding. His clothes hung on him like a human coat hanger. He gave me a brave smile and motioned to get in.

"Hi, Mr. X," I said while putting on my seatbelt. "Where are we headed?"

"You'll see," he said. His voice was as thin as his body.

"I wanted to tell you in person," I said. "I won a competition at work by giving a presentation on zero-based budgeting. I wanted to say thank you for turning me on to the concept. The prize for winning is a trip for two to Catalina Island. I can't wait to take Stephanie there!"

"Oh, good," Mr. X replied. "That's terrific news, Nicky. Although I'm surprised that a place like Big Rock would adopt something like ZBB." *Nicky? I'd never liked it when people called me that. But from Mr. X, it was endearing.*

"Yeah, I was very excited to win. Who knows if they'll actually use it," I said. *I knew the answer, but didn't want to admit defeat to Mr. X.* "And there's more. I'm a junior analyst right now, but there's an opening for an analyst position that I'm gunning for. It would be a sizeable pay raise, and my family sure could use the extra income." *Desperately, I didn't add.* "Big Rock is big on competitions, so they're giving the position to whoever presents the best big idea to the higher-ups. I have about a month to come up with something that will blow their socks off. Any ideas?"

"Well, knowing what I do about your current employer, you have two choices. You can pick an idea that would actually help them, and know you'll lose the promotion. Or you could choose an idea that is flashy and gives you a chance to win, but won't be of much use to anyone. It's an interesting philosophical question: would you rather win their game, or would you rather be useful? That's as much as I can tell you, but I'll think about it a little more." *Ugh, Vance was the clear front runner for the promotion. If he ended up as my boss, there'd be a pink slip in my future. I needed something bigger than cryptic philosophy from Mr. X.*

I was feeling pouty all of a sudden and wanted to change the subject. "So I assume from this week's Buffett quote that we're going to be talking about mergers and acquisitions?"

"That's correct," Mr. X said, lighting up in a way that betrayed his feeble body. Our business lessons were a frequency that always resonated with him.

"Have you ever done a merger or acquisition at Cootie?" I asked. *I knew the answer from our previous conversations, but let's tee up a softball for the old man. And maybe if we cover enough ground, he'll have a bright idea for my presentation.*

"Yes, several actually," he replied. "There's a lot of nuance that goes into that decision."

"Can you walk me through it?" I asked.

"The first thing you have to examine is your own motivations for wanting to do a deal. Be truly honest with yourself about why you want to do it."

"That's probably easier said than done," I said.

"Indeed. Let me first give you the wrong reasons for doing a deal. And unfortunately, these are what drive a lot of the behavior I see. First is just the thrill of action--to be in the game, to make something happen, even if it's stupid. Humans have a tendency to follow leaders who are bold. It must have been a survival mechanism of some kind." *I loved how Mr. X could weave a tapestry from the threads of business, psychology, and biology.*

"The second wrong reason is size, status, and ego. You can't discount the *BBQ factor*."

"What's the BBQ factor?" I asked.

"Being able to brag to your friends and family at the BBQ," he said.

"Oh, I see."

"Telling them how you're a big shot who runs a large company with more revenue, more employees, more assets, more complexity. Prestige is an awfully stupid reason for M&A. Like a bad king, you create a larger empire but with poorer citizens," he said.

"Is there a third wrong reason?" I said, keeping him rolling.

"I'll classify the third as general overconfidence," he continued. "If you've had some recent success, you might think you're on a hot streak. Many don't appreciate the dynamics of luck and skill in complex systems. Your hot streak may have a lot less to do with your abilities than you think."

"Can you explain that a little more?" I asked.

"Well, overconfidence can show up in something as simple as lofty expectations about what the two companies will look like when combined into one. It's called 'synergy,' assuming that two plus two will later equal five. There are generally two types of synergies. Can you guess what they are?"

The M&A note a few days before had prompted me to do some research in hopes of impressing Mr. X. "Revenue and cost synergies?" I said.

"Very good!" he said. *Hey, why was he so surprised?* His small outburst of excitement triggered a coughing fit that had me genuinely worried it would never stop. After a time, Mr. X regained himself. "You've really come a long way since our first meeting." I just smiled. "You can basically forget about revenue synergies where two businesses sell more just because they're combined. It hardly ever happens, and never to the degree that's projected. Businesses are rarely complimentary in that way."

"What about cost synergies due to sharing expenses between two businesses?" I asked.

"Those can be real, especially in the back office. It depends on how well each of the companies are run in their *strategic* versus *non-strategic* expenses before the merger. But even real cost synergies will come up short against overconfident projections. Deals fail in practice, but they never fail in projections."

"So I guess my takeaway for synergies should be that you shouldn't go into any M&A deal expecting miracles?" I said.

"That's right," he said. "Hail Marys are for church and the football field."

We pulled up in front of a competitor's burger joint. It had less curb appeal than the Cootie Burgers I had visited, but this chain did have a reputation for standout fries. "What are we doing here?" I asked Mr. X.

"Just doing a little research," he said cryptically as he motioned to exit the car. The driver hopped out and pulled out a wheelchair from the trunk. He helped Mr. X get settled into the chair and told us that he'd wait in the parking lot. I pushed Mr. X up the ramp and into the restaurant, out of the cold.

"What should I order?" I asked Mr. X as we stood in line. I wanted to help with the research.

"Whatever sounds good," he instructed. "Make sure you get fries; they're quite good."

"OK, what would you like?" I asked.

"I'm not hungry--thank you though," he said. "And as usual, please let me pay as a small thank you for all the traveling you do to come see me." *I really didn't mind. It rivaled my hikes with Steph as the favorite thing on my calendar.*

We ordered and I rolled Mr. X to a table that accommodated his chair. I saw Mr. X looking around in evaluation, no doubt sliding straws around in his head. It was a habit I had picked up from my unlikely mentor whenever I interacted with a business. *Simply unthinkable to the Nick from a year ago.* We continued our lesson.

"Let's discuss how a deal gets financed," Mr. X said. "It's a critical part of the merger and acquisition calculus."

"OK, like what?" I asked.

"The first choice is to use cash you have in the bank. The second is usually to issue debt to fund your acquisition. Remember back to our conversations about pine cones and 1980s junk bonds?"

"I do," I said.

"Eventually you run out of your own cash and people who are willing to loan you more money. So what does that leave you with?"

"Equity?" I guessed.

"That's right. The first thing you must understand is that equity--stock--is like having your own currency. If you issue shares for an acquisition, it's like printing your own currency. At the same time, you are effectively selling part of your business. Therefore, a sound rule of thumb is that you never issue shares unless you receive as much intrinsic business value as you're giving up."

"I think I follow, but can you give me a concrete example?"

"Sure," Mr. X replied. "Let's use a very simple example from my youth. Say you're in charge of your family's 100 acre farm. You decide to merge your farm with your neighbor's fifty acre farm into an equal partnership. You are now in charge of 150 acres, which is nice to talk about at BBQs, but your family's ownership of land and the crop yield has actually gone down by twenty-five acres."

"From 100 acres down to 75," I said after pretending not to be counting on my fingers.

"You're now in charge of 150 acres, but are you really much of a hero?" he asked.

"No, you were inflating your ego at the expense of your family," I said.

"There are obviously other factors in this decision, but you see the BBQ factor all the time in Corporate America," he said. "You should always ask yourself if you would sell one hundred percent of your business on the same basis as you're considering issuing equity."

"I see, so could you say that if you issue shares for less than intrinsic business value, you are harming your current family of shareholders? And if you are able to issue shares at above intrinsic value, you might actually be benefiting them?"

"That's right, Nicky!" he said. "I'm happy to hear you're thinking about the shareholders. If you're able to use your stock that's priced at twice what you know it's worth to acquire a company for half what it's worth, it doesn't take a genius to figure out you stand to add a lot of value for your shareholders. That'd be the equivalent of using fifty of your family's acres to acquire 100 of your neighbor's acres. I have to warn you now, few think this way. They want to get the most acres under management, regardless of how it might hurt those they've promised to serve."

"You do earn that 'rebel' nickname, don't you?" I teased. "What are some other ideas to keep in mind for M&A?"

"Here's a good one," he said. "Never trust pitch books put together by investment bankers. It's funny--they can give you precise numbers for what a business will earn ten years into the future, but they can't tell you what their own business will earn next month. That reminds me of a story."

"I love your stories..." At this point my burger and fries had arrived at the table. I tore into them while Mr. X continued talking. Everyone was right; the fries were exceptional. Piping hot, salty, crispy on the outside, smooth on the inside.

"A man has an ailing horse," Mr. X said. "He takes it to the vet and asks: 'Can you help me? Sometimes my horse walks just fine and sometimes he limps.' The vet replies: 'No problem--when he's walking fine, sell him.'" With this Mr. X laughed as heartily as his feeble body would allow and paid the price with a vicious coughing fit. It was bad enough that restaurant patrons looked on with concern, wondering if they should call for help. I nodded to them in reassurance, hopeful that it would pass soon. I saw more crimson on his handkerchief and my heart sank.

"I see," I said after the spell had subsided. "Others might only be looking to sell their business horses when they're walking well, not when they're limping. So always buyer beware."

"That's right," he said before taking a few deep breaths to regroup. "When you look at the historical data, the average premium paid has been around fifty percent above market prices. Because of that, as a general rule of thumb, most deals benefit the target company's shareholders at the expense of the acquiring company's shareholders."

"So the seller usually wins?" I said.

"Yes, the acquirer overpays, often due to the overoptimism we talked about before. Here's something else: CEOs are herd animals. They travel in packs and emulate each other, including when it comes to M&A. There's a first-mover advantage to being early in the cycle because there are more higher quality targets, fewer competitors, and usually lower valuations early on. Beware buying anything late in the cycle when everyone wants in. Usually the biggest and most colossally stupid activity occurs late in the game, near the top."

"What the wise man does in the beginning, fools do in the end," I said.

"Yes, there's even this phenomenon called the 'skyscraper index,'" he said.

"What's that?"

"There exists an odd correlation between a city setting a new record for the tallest building in the world and that city's real estate market crashing shortly thereafter. It happened with the Empire State Building in 1929, Sears Tower in 1973, Dubai in 2009. Having the tallest building is good for BBQ bragging rights. The biggest mistakes show up at the top of the cycle when optimism is running wild. And don't forget," he added. "When you are considering acquiring a company, think back to our conversation at the empty lot and the different ways to put a roof over the customers' heads."

"I know what you mean," I said. "Ask yourself, is it a better deal to get the roof through acquisition or potentially building it yourself? Or even some other creative means."

"That's right. And never participate in auctions," he said, shaking his finger at me. "You'll overpay when bidding against others. Bidding wars are bad news for acquiring shareholders."

"So are you thinking about acquiring this restaurant chain?" I asked conspiratorially.

"I'm considering it," he replied in hushed tones. "There are some obvious cost synergies and a lot of non-strategic expenses that we could wring out of their operations to improve profitability."

"So what's holding you back?" I asked.

"I'm worried that we'd be paying too much," he replied. "I don't think we have a big enough margin of safety."

"What does 'margin of safety' mean here?" I said.

"It originated as an engineering concept," he said. "When engineers build a bridge that's rated for 10,000 pounds, they only let trucks that weigh up to 5,000 pounds use it. There's a built in margin of safety, just in case. You don't go near the edge."

"Makes sense, but what does that have to do with this burger joint?" I asked.

"Well, what if I'm wrong on what I think this business is worth?" he said. "Imagine if I thought it was worth one hundred dollars, but I was wrong and it was only worth seventy-five. In order to leave myself a margin of safety, I'd only consider buying when I can pay fifty dollars. Then when I'm wrong, it can still work out OK."

"I can see how waiting for half-off deals would require a lot of patience," I said. He touched the tip of his nose with one index finger and pointed the other one at me, signaling I was right. Maybe he was just conserving oxygen.

"One last thing," he said. "We started this conversation talking about cash on the balance sheet being used for acquisitions. I believe a company's balance sheet should be run conservatively, even if it means slower growth. I'll admit, there's a redundancy to carrying extra cash and very little debt. Yes, it's expensive to maintain and I bet your MBA professors would say it's suboptimal. And I know Big Rock would vehemently disagree with me. But we have two kidneys for a reason--increasing our chances of survival. In the business case, we're talking about more than just the company's survival. Well-run corporations serve a critical social function. They need to be financially strong enough to act as economic shock absorbers to protect employees, suppliers, and customers from the volatilities of capitalism. Free markets can do strange things to find the right price level. It's unfortunate, but it's still the best system we have for coordinating human action. You need a conservative balance sheet to be a healthy shock absorber. Business done well actually protects the little guys from natural fluctuations." *Another pang of cognitive dissonance. I couldn't fight it--each trip to Wichita chipped away at my distrust of capitalism. What are you doing to me, Mr. X?!*

A thought crossed my mind: why was Mr. X doing research on a competitor when he seemed to be so close to Death's door? Why would this be a worthwhile use of his limited time left on Earth? The answer sprang to mind as quickly as the question had formed: business was what lit him up inside. It was his passion and seemed to roll back the clock. Or at least pause time. Business was all he had in this world.

I found myself feeling sorry for my billionaire friend.

CHAPTER 33

My next trip to Wichita would prove to be my oddest yet. I received my customary quote a few days before my flight:

> *"In allocating Berkshire's capital, we ask three questions: Should we keep the capital or pay it out to shareholders? If pay it out, then you have to decide whether to repurchase shares or issue a dividend. To decide whether to retain the capital, we have to answer the question: do we create more than $1 of value for every dollar we retain? Historically, the answer has been yes and we hope this will continue to be the case in the future, but it's not certain. If we decide to retain and invest the capital, then we ask, 'What is the risk?', and seek to do the most intelligent thing we can find. The cost of a deal is relative to the cost of the second best deal."* - Warren Buffett

My flight was delayed, and it was already dusk when I arrived. I was to report straight to Mr. X's house. My taxi battled the stream of traffic escaping downtown toward the sleepy suburbs of Wichita. We wove down side streets into a tree-lined neighborhood. The houses were nicely built brick structures, but not what you'd ever imagine for a billionaire. We pulled in front of a house that looked remarkably unremarkable. I double-checked the address; sure enough, it was the place. I paid the taxi and hopped out into the cool evening air.

There were lights on throughout the house and cars parked on both sides of the street. As I approached the front door, I could hear the din of voices mingling into a dull roar. There was clearly a party happening. I knocked, and after a few beats, someone I didn't know answered the door. I nodded apologetically and entered without a word.

Mr. X's house was appointed with well-worn craftsman style furniture. It wasn't fancy, but it had a timeless appeal to it. *Sort of like the old man himself.* I made my way to the living room where I found the critical mass of the party. I noticed Mr. X propped up in a hospital bed in the middle of the room, chatting with a few elderly gentlemen.

Cathy noticed my arrival and came over with a hug. "I was worried you weren't going to make it," she said, squeezing the life out of me.

"Sorry, there were mechanical issues with my plane," I said, after regaining my air.

"That's OK," she said. "You're just in time for the main event. I'm not sure if you know why you're here, but in case it isn't obvious, this is a living funeral for Mr. X. Although I much prefer the term *celebration of life*," she said. "He didn't want this, but when I told him it gives those we leave behind a sense of closure, he eventually gave in."

"You can be very persuasive," I said. Cathy chuckled.

"There's food in the kitchen," she said. "Cootie hamburgers and fries, of course. We even brought in a milkshake machine. Help yourself." With that she returned back to her previous conversation. I was starving after a long day, and Cathy's words were music to my ears. I reappeared from the kitchen with a plate full of food and found a place to sit and eat. I was only a few bites in when Cathy hushed the crowd.

"Thank you for joining us," she addressed the room. "We're all here to pay tribute to an amazing man." Mr. X writhed slightly in his bed. It was unclear if his discomfort was due to illness or the crowd's attention. She continued, "Mr. X has been like a father to me…" Cathy was choked up and stared down at the floor for a few moments as she regained her composure. "Sorry, this is supposed to be a celebration," she said with a little laugh through the tears. "Mr. X has been like a father to me," she restarted. "And I'm not sure what we'll do when he's gone. Well, I know what I'll be doing... going on a long vacation. And since I won't be running all his errands, I'll have a lot more free time." Everyone laughed, knowing the burden Cathy shouldered. "Joking aside, I was a young single mother, no education, no credentials, no future, when Mr. X took me on as his assistant. There were more qualified candidates, and I'll never understand why he chose me. He mentored me and gave me space and encouragement to grow. I'll always feel overwhelming gratitude that he took a chance on me. Thank you, Mr. X," she said. Cathy leaned down to the hospital bed to kiss his cheek. "Now, who wants to go next?"

It was quiet for a few beats. Eventually a brave soul raised his hand and told a similar story of Mr. X believing in him when no one else did. How Mr. X took a chance on him, and how it defined the trajectory of his career. Now that the seal was broken, a steady flow of such stories came forth. Some shared funny business predicaments that Mr. X helped them out of. Mr. X was also the butt of several good-natured jokes.

All of the stories were related to business. His personal life was conspicuously absent. *Were any family members even here? His work life really was everything to him.*

Eventually the stream slowed to a trickle. Mr. X raised his hand feebly. "I want to thank everyone for coming and sharing their stories." A coughing fit overtook him. We looked on in concern as we waited for him to recover. "It means a tremendous amount. You're all important to me... some more than others." *Always the jokester.* "I've had a good life. I honored my father's wishes and did the best I could to be useful and run the restaurant. Now that burden falls to you. I know you'll do an even better job than I did. Now get out, this old man needs his beauty sleep." He shooed away with his hand

and rolled slowly onto his side and seemed to already be asleep. *I guess the old man wasn't much for sentimental speeches.*

People started shuffling toward the door, finding their coats, and saying their goodbyes. Cathy caught up with me and told me to stick around. I hung back until it was just me, Cathy, a snoozing Mr. X, and an in-home nurse who must have been hiding in a back room.

"I hope you don't mind hanging around for a bit," Cathy said. "He usually doesn't sleep for more than an hour or two at a time. He told me it was important he speak with you."

"No problem," I told Cathy. "I'll catch up on some work while I wait."

"Thank you," she said. "There is a spare bedroom down the hall that is all ready for guests. You can stay here tonight."

I thanked her and I settled in to half-heartedly peck away at my homework. I wasn't in the mood. I got up and wandered around the house, finding Mr. X's office. It was similar to the rest of the house: solid but not flashy. I glanced around without going in too deep and invading his privacy. There were books everywhere. There were several framed pictures of Mr. X shaking hands with business people and dignitaries I didn't recognize. Slowly, I meandered back to the living room.

"See anything interesting in there?" Mr. X asked quietly, but still startling me.

"Sorry, I was just curious what the office of a billionaire looks like," I replied.

"Not that impressive, right?" he said. I just nodded and smiled. "How'd you like my party?"

"It was great," I said. "I loved hearing all the old stories. You've made a difference in a lot of people's lives."

"I've always strived to give more than I take. I believe the way I could do the most to help my fellow man was to do good through business. Truth be told, I hate being the center of attention like that," he said. "The spotlight makes me nervous. My mother would have beat me red with her purse if she found me showboating in front of a crowd." He laughed and coughed mightly. I felt helpless.

Mr. X's nurse peeked her head out as his cough was subsiding. She made her way to his bed and attached supplemental oxygen tubing to his nose. "This should help," she said with a pat of his chest.

"Thank you," he said, drawing in labored breaths. She disappeared again as quickly as she'd appeared. It was comforting to know that I had help should a medical emergency arise. *I'm not the right guy for that kind of responsibility.*

Once his breathing settled, Mr. X continued. "I wanted you to stick around so we could cover some more material. I don't have the energy to help others like I once did. But I want to give you as much ammo as I can to help you with this book. What you write will be important, Nicky. You'll have to inspire people into thinking for themselves and rebelling against the status quo."

"Always the rebel, eh Mr. X? I feel like I've learned a lot in our time together," I said. I was feeling an uncomfortable mixture of awe and uncertainty, with a smattering of pride mixed in that he trusted me with such a weighty responsibility.

"But not enough yet," he said. My internal balloon sagged a little with his comment. "Shall we get started on this visit's lessons and see if we can make up ground?"

"Only if you feel up to it," I said, sitting down next to his bed.

"You just try to keep up." I patted his inert leg. "One of the things that's missing today in corporations is a feeling of partnership between shareholders, the board of directors, and management. If more CEOs viewed their shareholders as business partners, they'd do things a lot differently."

"Like what?" I asked.

"Let me ask you," he said. "If a CEO viewed it as her job to take care of her shareholders, at what price would she want her company's stock to trade?"

"I guess she'd want it to be as fair to everyone as possible?" I said.

"That's a good start," he said. "So how could she keep the playing field level so they weren't taking advantage of each other?"

I thought for a moment while he seemed to be concentrating on breathing. I finally said, "Ideally, you'd want the price of a share to change hands at the exact intrinsic value of the business. That way, both the exiting partner and the new incoming partner are each getting their money's worth."

"That's right," he said with a new vigor. *I wasn't sure if it was the supplemental oxygen or talking about business that was revitalizing him.* "One of your responsibilities as the CEO of a publicly traded company is to make sure partners who need liquidity are able to get it. You don't know what's going on in their lives and why they might need cash. Maybe they have a sick relative they're taking care of. Or maybe they have a charity project that desperately needs funding. I believe you have a moral obligation to make sure they aren't taken advantage of when they sell. Does that make sense?"

I nodded. *The old man's sense of fairness and morality definitely didn't mesh with the stereotype of the money-grubbing tycoon. He was performing quiet, heroic corporate deeds that no one knew about.*

"We have a policy at Cootie Burger," he said. "We will make our best effort to provide liquidity to any partner who needs to get out. At a minimum, we'll give them dollar-for-dollar what the accountants say the net worth of the company is. We think the partners should benefit from the business doing well, not by taking advantage of each other through opportunistic buying and selling."

"That sounds fair, but how do you actually do all of that?" I asked.

"It's actually simpler in practice than it sounds in theory. Our policy is to do corporate share buybacks any time the company's stock price approaches that accounting net worth number, also known as *book value*. We'll put in buy bids at book value should the stock trade down to that level. We buy back a partner's shares and make sure those who really need the cash can access it without being harmed."

"So that would mean the price of your stock will never go below book value?" I said.

"Well, if everyone decided they wanted to sell at once, we wouldn't be able to meet them at book value," he said. "They would overwhelm our cash balances. But we make our best effort, and I think our partners appreciate it. In fact, even announcing our intentions has a way of putting a floor under our stock price. If you were one of the partners and knew that we intended to give you at least book value, you'd have to be pretty desperate to sell for anything less than that. If you gave us enough time, we'd likely make sure you got book value."

"I've noticed you are using the term *partners* instead of *shareholders*. Why is that?" I asked.

"Legally, there isn't a big difference in terms," he said. "But I purposely refer to Cootie shareholders as 'partners' for a reason. Word choices impact our thoughts. If I think of them as my partners in the business, I make better decisions on their behalf. Not everyone thinks this way, but I'm not just their CEO. I serve as their fiduciary. I take full responsibility for their financial well-being with respect to our stock. I want to be an example of the good that can come from business done right."

"I understand why you put in a floor by doing stock buybacks," I said. "What do you do when the stock price goes too far in the other direction and becomes overly optimistic? It seems like if it's too high, the outgoing partner wins and the new incoming partner is starting at a disadvantage."

"That's a very good insight," he said. *Warm feelings.* "Too much enthusiasm for our stock can be hard to control. Our only move is to try and talk our stock down from that ledge."

"What do you say then?" I asked.

"We tell everyone we believe the price of the stock has gotten out in front of the true worth of the business. What we refer to as *intrinsic value*."

"Do you tell people what you think that intrinsic value number is?" I inquired.

"Let me first ask you a question," he said. "What determines the intrinsic value of a business? Said another way, assuming you had perfect information, what would you add up to come up with a single number?"

This concept has recently come up in school, and I had tucked the information away in case this question should arise. I said proudly, "The intrinsic value is the net present value of all of the cash that can be taken out of the business during its remaining life."

"Alright," he said. "But how about in plain English?" *Ummm...*

"Isn't it nothing more than counting the cash in the business now and what we expect will be there in the future?" I said.

"That's better," he said. "The truth is, there's no single right answer for intrinsic value. In fact, the right way to think about it is a probability distribution of outcomes that form a range of prices."

"What does that mean?" I said.

"Think about it. There are different future scenarios which lead to very different amounts of cash in the bank," he replied patiently. "What if there's a recession? What if competition intensifies? What if in the case of Cootie, people stop eating hamburgers?"

"That's hard to imagine given what I ate earlier," I said. "I've yet to have a bad meal."

"I think you're generally right, but dietary habits change over time, just like anything else. There's a persistence to technology--the longer it's been around, the longer it's likely to be around. Remember our chairs-on-Mars conversation?"

"I do. Are you saying two buns and a patty are a *technology*?" I asked.

"Sure, they fulfill a human need or desire, don't they? And they keep you from getting ketchup and mustard on your hands," he said. "Now where was I before you derailed us?"

"I think you were explaining how to figure out what a business is worth?"

"Ah, yes. So the total amount of cash a business generates in its lifetime could be a lot of different numbers based on what happens in the world. There's so much that can go right and wrong. Anyone who says they have exact numbers about the future is dangerously overconfident. There's more though..." he said, pausing for a brief coughing session.

"Keep going," I said quietly when he'd recovered.

"You said the intrinsic value is based on the net present value, right?" he asked.

"Yes, but what does that actually mean?"

"All it says is that a dollar today is worth more than a dollar tomorrow. Likewise, a dollar available ten years from now is worth quite a bit less than a dollar in your pocket today. Do you know what dictates how much less it will be worth?"

"Isn't it interest rates?" I said.

"That's right, have you been studying without me?" he said. "The higher the interest rate, the less that dollar ten years from now is worth. So even if we had a crystal ball and knew the exact quantity of cash that we'd get out of our business from here to eternity, different interest rate assumptions would make that pile of cash worth more or less today. You can start to see why interest rates have a big effect on asset values. They're like the gravity of the financial world. They're everywhere and always tugging."

"The interest rates on my credit cards feel like a black hole," I said.

"Be careful with those," he said. "They're like financial barnacles."

"No kidding, where were you a few years ago to tell me that?" I said. "So when interest rates are low, there's less discount applied to the pile of cash, so the intrinsic value appears higher. Which in turn makes the prices of everything higher. Am I thinking about that right?"

"You are," he said. "But don't forget, there's no single interest rate. Just like there's no single point of gravity in the universe. There are different rates for different risk and reward profiles. Did you know that the sun is 99.8% of the mass of our solar system?"

"I didn't. I guess it's pretty big."

"Indeed. Well, the sun in our financial solar system are the central banks. They have a huge effect on interest rates. Given humanity's track record with managing complex environments, it's surprising we'd trust a handful of academic bureaucrats to decide the amount of gravity. But I'm getting us way off track."

"That's OK." *That's usually my job.*

"Back to what we tell our partners," he said. "Very smart people could look at the exact same set of facts and calculate two different intrinsic values based on their view of the future. There's nothing wrong with that-- diverse views make for healthy markets. We simply provide all the facts as clearly as we can, just as we'd want to see them if the tables were turned. It's the best we can do to be fair to our partners. Back to your original question about intrinsic value... a few words of caution."

"I'm all ears," I said.

"My observation is that CEOs and managers are like most investors and prefer the safety of the crowd," he said. "They have a penchant for buying back their stock in boom periods when all is rosy and the general market is going up. Optimism fills the air. This behavior favors outgoing shareholders who sell back to the company at inflated prices. Incoming and remaining shareholders are harmed because value has walked out the door."

"I have a question," I said. "If you're a CEO, but you know from experience you aren't a very good investor, what can you do?"

"Let me reframe your question," he said. "What if you're a CEO, and you have no idea what the intrinsic value of your business is? What do you do then?"

"Yes, that's better."

"You should quit," he said.

"Seriously?"

"No, I'm joking, but in my mind it's a dereliction of duty. If anyone were to have a sense what a business is worth, it should be the CEO in charge. It's one of your responsibilities as a steward of capitalism."

"Fair point," I said. "But what if that wasn't your strong suit?"

"One possible option is going to be the same as any investor who can't value a business. Use simple dollar cost averaging--nibble away over time by buying a little back regularly. You'll buy low sometimes, and too high others. Sometimes you'll benefit incoming shareholders. Other times it'll be the existing group who wins. The idea is those errors cancel each other out and come out in the wash. At least you aren't systematically favoring one side or the other and blindly following the corporate herd who usually buys too high."

"Not the most rebellious approach, but there's a logic to it," I said. "Two wrongs making a right."

"Something like that," he replied. "Another word of caution: I saw a survey of CFOs that was conducted in the middle of the last bubble. The vast majority of them could recognize that all of their competitors were dramatically overpriced. But only a small percentage thought their own company was too expensive. We're blind to our own circumstances."

"Steph told me about something like that," I said. "She called it the *endowment effect*. It showed that we generally think the things we own are worth more, just because we own them."

"Smart girl," he said. "It's very easy during the boom times to make projections that current success is inevitable. That the graph goes in a straight line up and to the right. But that's not how the world works. There are seasons and cycles--remember our humble pinecone? Reversion to the mean is incredibly powerful. It's easy to fool yourself otherwise and commit suicide by extrapolation."

"I see that a lot at Big Rock," I said.

"I can only imagine," he said. "Especially when that's what the boss wants to see. Let me change gears. How do you make money as an investor or business owner?"

"Assuming there's a market for shares of your company?" I asked.

"Sure," he said.

"The share price can go up and what you own can be worth more, so you can make money that way," I said.

"Not wrong, but let's add a little nuance to your thinking. When the underlying business becomes more profitable, the intrinsic value goes up and the share price tends to move upward as well. Sometimes it can take longer than you'd ever expect for share price and intrinsic value to converge, but they eventually do. So yes, share price appreciation is one way. Remember, you only get that money when you sell though. A lot can happen between the market's last quoted price and actual cash in your account."

"Like what?" I asked.

"Think about it this way," he said. "Say you and I owned a lemonade stand, fifty-fifty. I agreed to sell you my half for five billion dollars one day. The market price would say our company was worth ten billion based on that transaction. The next day you agree to sell it to me for fifty billion. The headlines would read we own a one-hundred billion dollar company based on the market price. Is our lemonade stand really worth that, just because of two transactions? Are either one of us really billionaires?"

"You still are, but not because of the lemonade stand," I said. "I get your point. The quote on your investment has to be taken with a grain of salt until it's actually liquid and in your pocket."

"You said it better than I did," he said.

"First time for everything," I shot back.

"What's another way for you get paid on your investment and business ownership?"

"If the company pays out dividends?" I said.

"Yes, and you might be surprised to learn that almost everyone is doing dividends wrong," he said.

"Hard to imagine a rebel allocator like you has that opinion," I joked. "How so?"

"I'm not actually a rebel," he said. "Just someone who uses common sense in a world where too few do. But back to dividends. Most executives believe that once they pay a dividend, they have to keep paying it. Maybe even increase it a little every year. They think they have to give the shareholders their allowance to keep them happy. It becomes the price to rent capital and keep their shareholders at bay."

"That sounds logical," I said.

"I guess it is to an extent," he said. "It's not entirely the fault of management. Shareholders have been conditioned to expect a little treat every year, so CEOs are doing what they think they must to keep the natives from getting restless. But it's dead wrong."

"How should they think about it?" I asked.

"If you're one of the partners in a successful business, you should want to keep as much of your money as possible invested there. That assumes the business is doing good things with the money, by which I mean earning high returns on invested capital and redeploying the money intelligently. Do you remember our lessons on ROIC and compounding?"

"Yes," I said.

"The same magic of compounding can happen inside a company when a high ROIC strategy has a long runway to absorb a lot of capital and keep providing high returns. It acts like a golden goose," he said. "If you're an investor, you want management to unlock the compounding machine inside the business. Then you have to do all you can *not* to take any money out of it. You want to keep your money tied up in this machine that feeds itself and keeps growing. Taking money out would be a terrible idea--including to pay a dividend."

"How might management think about dividends then?" I asked.

"Paying a dividend should be the last resort for a rebel allocator. It's like a confession that they have a lack of attractive ideas. It says a lot actually: I can't reinvest back in our business and find profitable growth. There are no acquisitions that would be productive for our partners. There are no marketable securities I could buy on your behalf that are undervalued. The price of our own stock is high enough to be inappropriate to buy back. In essence, they're saying I can't find anything smart to do with this money, so I'm giving it back to my partners."

"That really does say a lot," I said. "But I learned that something like eighty percent of public companies pay a dividend?" I asked.

"I believe the number for the S&P 500 is around there," he said.

"So your thinking on this is *quite* contrarian," I replied.

"It is," he said. "But that doesn't mean I'm wrong. In some instances, especially for an older, established company, paying a dividend could make sense. They may have a profitable business that simply can't absorb new reinvestment. They're out of other good opportunities and are sending the money back to owners. If that was the reasoning used, it's very honorable to pay a dividend rather than have the hubris of reinvesting in value-destroying projects. I'd call that commendable even. There are a lot of unforced errors made in Corporate America from trying to jam money into empire-building, self-congratulatory BBQ projects. It's slower to grow with the mindset of a good capital allocator, which is why it's so rare; but my belief is it's longer lasting." *Ouch, sorry Corporate America.* "There's another problem with dividends."

"What's that?" I asked.

"When a company issues a dividend, it gets applied to all of the owners equally. That may sound like a good idea to treat everyone the same, but what if you're an investor who doesn't have any use for the money at that time? Too bad, everyone has to take the dividend when the corporation says so."

"I see," I said. "Instead, the people who have expenses they need to pay can sell a little of their stock when they need the cash. For everyone else, they get to keep their money in and hopefully compounding. You get to self-select."

"Correct, a dividend takes away that freedom of choice. One of the arguments in favor of fat dividends is you can't trust management to make smart decisions with the money. A dividend takes the money out of management's hands before they do something boneheaded with it. If that's the case, I'd rather just find more capable management."

"Have you ever paid a dividend at Cootie?" I wondered.

"We haven't, despite some begging from shareholders and displeasure from the media. My thought has always been, if we can keep the money earning twenty percent for our partners, do they *really* want it back that badly? How are they planning to make that kind of return on their own? There have been a few points where we've come close to paying a dividend. The tax laws were changing to make dividends more favorable, and we didn't see a lot of great reinvestment options at the time. But with a little patience, opportunity came knocking, and we were back to work compounding our partners' money."

"So the answer on dividends is, *it depends*," I surmised.

"Yes, the same answer to most thoughtful questions," he said. "Now, it's getting late and I'm dreadfully tired. Like I could sleep forever," he said.

"Don't you go dying on me just yet, old man," I said. "I have a feeling we still have some important topics to cover."

"Indeed, we do," he said. "The guest bedroom is down the hall. If I don't see you in the morning, have a great trip to Catalina."

"I'm surprised you remembered," I said.

"I'm full of surprises," he said as he was nodding off.

I found the spare bedroom and crashed into bed. I was up before dawn to catch the earliest flight home. As I was leaving, I made my way passed Mr. X's hospital bed in the living room. He laid there serenely, breathing his assisted oxygen. The bed looked too big for him; his body was small under the blankets.

I couldn't help feeling choked up wondering how many visits we had left.

CHAPTER 34

Finally, our romantic vacation to Catalina Island! A getaway like this was just what Steph and I needed to rekindle the fire doused by our respective grinds.

It was a quick flight down to Long Beach and a taxi ride to the port terminal. From there, we caught the boat to the heart of Catalina, arriving on the island just in time for lunch. Our hotel check-in wasn't until 3pm, but they accepted our bags and recommended a brewhouse close by. We ordered a couple burgers and flights of different beers to sample. Life was good.

Stephanie seemed to be drinking her beers with an uncharacteristically aggressive pace. It wasn't long until she had blown through tipsy. *Slow down, hon… we just got here.*

She put a knife in the back of our small talk with a pointed look. "Nick… we need to talk." *The most dreaded four words in the English language.*

She began, "I've been thinking… our parents are so different. Yours don't seem to care what you do. Mine *definitely* care. They don't like that we're living together and not married. They tell me it's sinful. Whenever I see them, they make snippy remarks about it. It's really bothering me."

"OK," I said. "What do they want us to do? Find separate apartments again?"

"I don't know what they want," she said. "I don't know how to make them happy."

I never understood what the problem was with living together before you were married. Imagine the horror of only learning about your partner's "little quirks" *after* being locked down by holy matrimony. Who would ever roll those dice? What if she shed like a rottweiler or left clipped toenails on every flat surface? What if he shrunk all your clothes and liked playing trombone at two in the morning? *Sorry, no refunds--you're in it for the long haul.* People will test drive a car that they'll keep for two years, but not a living arrangement that's supposed to last forever. *Surely, you're joking, Mr. Feynman?*

She startled me back to reality, "Are you even listening to me?"

"Yeah, of course, babe. Do you think they want us to get married?"

"I don't know," she said. "They haven't said that. I don't think my dad wants us to."

"Your dad definitely doesn't want that," I said. "Don't you think we're a little young to get married?"

"Probably, but my parents were already married and had a family started by the time they were our age. And they seem happy."

"That was forty years ago when people only lived to sixty. What's the rush?" I asked.

"I guess there isn't a rush, but don't you want to know where this is going?" she said.

"They think I'm not good enough for you, don't they?" *Her dad made little effort to hide his disgust that his daughter was under-kicking her coverage.*

"What? Why are you making this about you?" Her eyes searched for something in mine. "I'm trying to share with you how I'm feeling," she said.

"Well, I don't know how to fix it," I replied.

"I'm not asking you to fix it," she said. "I just want you to understand."

"Why are you telling me about something if you don't want me to fix it?"

"God, you just don't get it," she said.

"What don't I get?"

"Nevermind."

We sat in silence until the check came. *Not exactly the best start to a romantic getaway.* I paid the bill, and we stepped out into a scene fit for a postcard. The views did nothing to mend the rift between us. Across the street, there was a bike shop. *I had an idea.* "Hey, I know. Let's rent some bikes and explore the island."

"Fine." *Clearly not fine.*

Being a busy Saturday, all the shop had left was a tandem bike. "We'll take it!" I said, hoping to turn our vacation around with some adventure. We wheeled the bike outside and made every effort to pedal away gracefully. I realized immediately that this plan was doomed. Riding a tandem bike turns out to be much harder than it looks. If both riders aren't on the same page and leaning in unison, it's incredibly difficult to steer. We were out of sync on all fronts, so no surprise we struggled to navigate the twisting, narrow island roads.

After a stretch of riding that involved more frustration and biting remarks than sightseeing, Stephanie asked if I had a plan beyond meandering all day. She wanted to know where we were going.

"I thought we could check out the botanical garden on the island. I read it's supposed to be really nice. I think it's just a few turns ahead," I said.

"No, Nick. I mean, where are we going with this relationship?" *Oh, she meant the existential where are going.*

"That's a big question, Steph."

"Well, I want to know what you're feeling." *Ugh, feelings.*

"I love spending time together. When we aren't on a tandem bike that is." *I had a bad habit of making jokes during serious conversations to add levity.*

"I'm serious. And what 'time' are you talking about? You're always so busy with work, school, and traveling to Wichita. We barely see each other despite living under the same roof."

A lot *had* changed in my life. I went from a starving journalism student with no girlfriend and lofty goals of changing the world, to a cog in a corporate wheel with a live-in girlfriend. "I know I'm busy," I said. "I don't even know how I ended up here. It feels like things just keep happening. Little steps I didn't realize I was taking."

"You mean with me?" She was starting to tear up. *Pull up! Pull up!*

"No, no. I meant with getting a job at Big Rock and going back to school. And then with Mr. X and Wichita. I felt like at every step I only had one move--keep going forward. Like I was being swept along by life."

"Maybe my dad is right," she said while staring off and shaking her head. "You don't know what you're doing. You aren't a real grown up yet."

I wanted to be angry and offended. But sometimes a statement rings so true it cuts you to the core, and you're incapable of response. Then the anger from your bruised ego finds a foothold.

"Whatever," I said. *Of course I'm not a real grown up.* I brooded as we struggled through a series of turns. My pocket started chirping with a phone call.

"Pull over, please," I said in a huff. "I have to take this."

It was Cathy. Mr. X had taken a turn for the worse and was in the hospital. I was to get to Wichita as fast as possible for goodbyes. I hung up in a state of shock. I went from dull hot anger to an icy sharp knot in my stomach. *Had I already shared my last words with Mr. X? I hope not!* Cathy had hung up, but the phone remained by my ear as I stared off vacantly.

"What is it?" she asked.

"I have to go," I said, catatonic.

"What?!" she snapped. "Go where? This was supposed to be our weekend, Nick!"

"Wichita… Mr. X is summoning me."

"Summoning? Like you're his butler? It can't wait until Monday?" she said.

"He's in the hospital and may not have until Monday," I said.

"That's terrible news," she said. "But you know, old people go into the hospital all the time. We're still having *regular* last visits with my grandma. Stay here with me please."

"I can't. I have to go."

"OK," she said, tearing up. "If you have to go, go. I guess I'll just stay here and enjoy a romantic vacation *for two*." I didn't know what else to say other than that I was sorry.

I pulled up the ferry schedule on my phone. If I hustled, I might make the next boat off the island. I didn't have time to make the necessary relationship repairs. That conversation would take hours. *Days? Decades?*

I yelled another apology over my shoulder as I ran off, leaving her by herself on a tandem bike by the side of the road. *Who said chivalry isn't dead?*

CHAPTER 35

I made the ferry and caught a red eye out of Southern California bound for the Midwest. I slept in fits and starts on the plane. My stomach was in ropes, my world spinning off its axis. I flagged a cab and arrived at the hospital just as the sun was pushing at the horizon. The sky was a marbled slate gray. The promise of a new day couldn't have felt less authentic.

I checked into the hospital and bought some overpriced flowers from the gift shop. I found the elevator and made my way to Mr. X's room. He was sleeping, small and frail in the hospital bed. Machines beeped loudly as they monitored his vitals and fed him oxygen to keep him alive. Cathy was loyally asleep in a window nook that doubled as a bed, if you could call it that. I quietly took a chair near Mr. X's bed and tried not to disturb either of them. My thoughts went back to how I'd left things in shambles in Catalina. A nurse came in to check on Mr. X, rousing Cathy from her sleep. She greeted me warmly with a hug, as was her superpower.

"How's he doing?" I asked.

"He's hanging in there… barely," she said, fighting back the emotions of the inevitable. "I've been here all night. If you wouldn't mind taking a shift, I'd love to run home to shower and change my clothes."

"Of course," I replied. I felt dirty myself from the red eye, but I didn't want to complain. Anyway I had left all my stuff behind in Catalina, so I had no way to freshen up even if I wanted to.

"Oh, and just so you aren't surprised, Mr. X's daughter, Mary, is on her way."

"I thought they weren't speaking anymore?" I asked.

"They weren't. But death has an odd way of reuniting people," she said. *Homespun Midwest wisdom.* "See you in a bit," she said, already halfway out the door.

Without opening his eyes, the old man said in a gravelly voice, "I thought you'd never make it."

I let out a cathartic laugh. "You ruined my vacation," I said.

"I know, I'm sorry. But we still have one lesson left."

"Wouldn't miss it for the world, Mr. X," I said, faking a brave smile.

"I don't have a lot of breaths left. But there are a few vital lessons I still need to give you." He paused to let his oxygen catch up. Even talking was a chore for him now.

"Mr. X, we don't need to..."

"Stop. Please, this is important to me," he said. "This lesson will give context to all our past talks."

"Yes, sir," I said. It seemed like a futile endeavour. He was too weak to teach and I wasn't in any mood to learn.

"The ancient Greeks famously said that the revisiting of definitions is the beginning of wisdom," he said. He must have been thinking about this session with an opening like that. "I realized that we never defined capital allocation in our early lessons."

"What is your definition of capital allocation, Mr. X?" I said. *Might as well be a good sport and support the last wishes of my dying friend.*

"At the most basic level, it's how you decide to spend money. But it's even deeper than that. Successful capital allocation means converting inputs like money, materials, energy, ideas, human effort, into more valuable outputs. It's that transformation process."

"That just sounds like business to me," I said.

"You're right. It reminds me of a joke," he said. *Do we have time for jokes?* He stopped to sip some water from a plastic straw inserted into one of those weird yellow hospital jugs.

"Please, do tell," I said.

"Two young fish swim by an older fish," he wheezed. "The elder says, 'Morning boys, how's the water?' The two younger fish swim on. Eventually one looks at the other and says, 'What the hell is *water*?'" With this he let out a surprisingly loud laugh that sent him coughing. I couldn't help but smile at how he cracked himself up, even at Death's door.

"You see," he said when he'd recovered. "Capital allocation is baked into all of business, every decision. Like water surrounding the fish--we don't notice until it's pointed out to us."

"While we're backtracking a little, can I ask a question I should have asked months ago?" I said.

"Absolutely."

"What the hell is capital anyway? Is it just money? Or machinery? Or buildings? I feel like I've heard it used in so many different contexts; I'm not even sure how to define it."

"That's a very good question, Nicky," he said. "It is a foundational term that is often misunderstood. People use the term to describe so many different things, it makes the definition become fuzzy and sloppy. The Inuits have fifty different words for snow, yet we suffer with one word that strains to explain a wide variety of things. You'll laugh, but I've invented my own word to help my thinking."

"What is it?" I asked.

"Before we get into my made-up words, let me tell you my definition of capital," he said. "I view capital as goods, both tangible and intangible, that were previously produced that aren't directly satisfying a human need yet. Capital is whatever bits, atoms, or energy that are available to eventually produce something that delights a customer. An example might help?"

"Yes, please."

"Let's pretend you live alone on a deserted island," he said. I was happy to see that teaching was having a small revitalizing effect on him. "You can either pick berries to eat, or sit and stare out at the ocean. You need berries to survive, but you also like sitting on your butt and taking in the surf."

"Yes, I do," I said. "Probably more than most." He just smiled.

"You could decide to forgo picking berries for a few hours and use that time to fashion a stick that would pick berries faster. You have to go without berries for a while to create this stick. You're delaying gratification today in favor of a better future. By the way, the same principles on the desert island apply to an individual company, a family, a nation, or a global economy. The exercise of foresight, restraint of appetites, anticipation of future demand, a lowering of time preferences, delaying consumption today so you can consume more in the future--they all apply."

"I think I'm following," I said. "Keep going."

"That stick which allows you to gather more berries *is capital.* It doesn't directly satisfy your need to eat, but it delights you with more berries. Without capital, we'd all be living hand-to-mouth, barely surviving. So the more we save as a society and invest in our capital, the more sticks we create, the more berries we can all have. Make sense?"

"Yes," I said.

"Here's where the idiot Ph.D. economists get it wrong," he said. *Still a feisty rebel until the end.* "In their fancy equations and physics envy, they assume capital is this big blob of clay that can be reshaped at a moment's notice. The term they use is *homogenous*--like homogenized milk. They assume your stick can be magically transformed into a wheelbarrow to haul your berries."

"That clearly seems wrong."

"It's dead wrong," he agreed. "In reality, capital is a historic relic of previous efforts. It's usually crafted for a specific purpose and becomes a sunk cost if it has no alternative use. I can't take a milkshake machine out of a restaurant and chop down a tree with it. Capital is mostly fixed and sunk, so it's vitally important that it's deployed wisely. Misallocated capital is of no use to anyone. It is a loss to the entrepreneur, the investor, and the consumer."

"Yes, I see," I said. "What was your made up term, before we get too far and forget?"

"You're going to laugh," he said. "The word is *fapital*, which is a portmanteau of financial and capital. Financial, capital… fapital. Fapital represents the ownership claim to real capital and productive capacity. I would put money, stocks, bonds, deeds, things like that in the fapital bucket. Fapital isn't the same as machinery or inventory, or even intangibles like ideas and patents. Those are capital, and they're used for the eventual production that meets human wants and needs. Fapital is an abstraction. It's the claim to the means of production."

"I'll have to think about that one, but I like the idea of segmenting the real from the abstract." I wanted to stick with this concept, but there was something I needed to ask Mr. X while he was still with it. "There's something I just have to know: why is capital allocation so important to you? It seems like an obscure topic to get excited about."

He stared straight forward, letting out raspy breaths while he gathered his thoughts. "Have you ever seen those Russian stacking dolls?"

"Sure."

"It's like those dolls. Layer inside of layer. Or the water surrounding the fish. Let me see if we can work through the different layers so you can get a better understanding of what I mean. First, who has a stake in the success of a business?"

"Certainly the owners," I said.

"OK," Mr. X replied. "We'll call them shareholders in this context. Businesses that make great capital allocation decisions deliver higher returns for their shareholders. They earn higher returns on capital and they don't squander the money once they earn it. In fact, it's hard to imagine a higher-leverage effort for an investor than improving management's capital allocation skills."

"Speaking of management, they should have a vested interest in proper capital allocation, right?" I asked.

"Good, that's another layer," he said. "I believe the vast majority of CEOs want to do a good job. Unfortunately, most haven't been properly trained, at least not to where they'd feel comfortable setting an independent course for their companies. They don't teach much about capital allocation in school. I had to learn it slowly on my own through trial and error."

"I certainly haven't learned it in school yet," I concurred. "What about employees?"

"Of course. Anyone who has been restructured out of a job knows how awful it is," he said.

"That seems to happen all the time at the companies Big Rock acquires. Chopping the workforce is part of their blueprint."

"No doubt," he said. "When leaders choose projects, employees come naturally attached. When management makes the wrong decision and is forced to change course, the collateral damage rains down on the helpless employees. Writedowns, restructurings, and layoffs represent failures of past decisions, of bad capital allocation."

"How about customers who depend on a company for their various wants and needs?" I said. *Hit this one next, old timer.*

"Absolutely," he continued with a verve. "Remember back to our lesson on *strategic* versus *non-strategic* expenses. Good capital allocation means doing more with less to create happier customers. The pressure to continually deliver value is one of the wonders of the free market." *It was amazing how far I'd come in appreciating that sentiment.*

"You know," I said, "when I first met you, I thought business just existed to take advantage of the little guy. You've changed how I see the world."

"Thank you," he said. "You certainly had a long way to go to get there, but I knew it'd be worth the journey."

"A very long way," I said with a smile.

"Let's go down another layer," Mr. X continued. "Roll up all of those customers into society at large. When you are able to provide value for the least required cost, you free up resources that can go toward adding value somewhere else."

"Can you explain that a little more?" I asked.

"Sure. Imagine that inside you are all of these different locks. Each lock represents one of your wants or desires. You have a lock for food, a lock for shelter, a lock for water, a lock for the opposite sex." He paused to raise a joking eyebrow. *Still a feisty old codger.* "You get the idea. Now imagine that each capital allocation project creates one key. Ideally, the entrepreneur knows the lock their key will fit beforehand. A restaurant provides you food, a hotel gives you shelter, shoes protect your feet. The role of business is to use the least amount of resources to create the key that fits a certain lock. Doing a proper job spares resources to create more keys for other locks. In this sense, profit should be celebrated as a signal that an entrepreneur provided value while consuming the least amount of resources to do so. When all of society's businesses are properly allocating capital, more locks get keys, and we're all better off. That's all technology really is: the means for us to turn more locks using fewer and cheaper keys."

"I love that analogy, Mr. X," I said.

"And since you're from California," he continued, "you'll probably like this last one."

"Oh, boy…" I said playing along.

"It requires scarce resources to create all of our technology keys. From an ecological perspective, aren't we protecting the environment by properly marshalling our resources?"

"Sure," I said.

"Eliminating the waste of bad capital allocation is a step toward increasing resource productivity and the sustainability of our planet. Good capital allocation saves the environment, if you can believe it." *Huh, there's a mind-bender. Mr. X may have done more to protect the environment than my parents ever had with their ecological crusades.*

"There really are a lot of invisible layers," I said. "I think I understand why it's so important now."

"That's good, Nicky," he said warmly. "You have to promise me something before I'm gone."

"Anything, Mr. X." *A lump swelled in my throat.*

"Promise me that you'll give this book your best effort. I know how rare it is for a book to change the world. But if you throw even a small rock in the pond, you never know where the ripple might travel."

I took his hand and a tear escaped onto my cheek. "I promise I'll give you my best. You have my word." *I meant it to the core of my being.*

"Thank you, son," he said.

We both sat for a while until he fell asleep. Eventually Cathy returned and relayed the message that Mr. X's daughter was on her way. Cathy and I exchanged a worried look. We were both wondering if Mr. X could hold out until Mary got there.

Eventually Mary did arrive. *And boy, did she have a surprise for us.*

CHAPTER 36

A middle-aged woman stood in the hospital room doorway. Mr. X's eyes fluttered open, and a look of noticeable relief washed across his face. "Mary! Come in, please."

"Hi, Frank," she said. *Frank?* Her demeanor was cool, but her eyes suggested she had been crying not long ago.

As Mary entered the room, I noticed an elderly woman lingering in the hallway behind her. She reminded me of Jackie O. in her later years--classy and put-together. The elderly woman drew in a deep breath and walked toward the doorway. I'll never forget the look on the old man's face when he saw her. His mouth just hung open. He couldn't say a word.

"I brought someone with me," Mary said with the smile of a kid who had a secret.

"Hi, Frankie," the older woman said. I looked at Cathy for a clue to what was going on. She just stood there, completely in shock.

"Helen…" Mr. X said. "I thought… I thought I'd never see you again."

"I guess that was one promise I couldn't keep," she said. Mary and Helen came into the room, which suddenly felt too small. Cathy and I were clearly unintentional intruders to a very intimate moment. We beat a hasty retreat and shut the door behind us.

"Who is that older woman?" I asked outside. I was beyond confused at this point.

"Helen," she replied. "She's Mr. X's wife."

CHAPTER 37

"His wife…," I repeated dumbly. "I thought his wife... was dead?"

"Nope, she's alive and kicking. Obviously."

"Mr. X said on a few occasions that he'd lost her?" I said.

"He did--she left him more than twenty years ago," Cathy said.

"I had always assumed she'd passed away."

"No… well, it's complicated," she said. "Here's my understanding. She didn't want to live in the Midwest anymore. Mr. X didn't want to leave the business, so she left to pursue her own life. At least that's the story I was told." We settled into the waiting room. *How do I process the last five minutes?*

After a good while, a nurse appeared to notify us that Mr. X wanted to see us. We made our way back to the room and entered timidly. Whatever they'd talked about, the frost in the Xavier Family had thawed. Each woman had taken a side of the bed, each holding one of Mr. X's hands. Anyone who didn't know better would assume they were a normal, happy family and the last twenty years of strife had never happened. Cathy and I stood at the foot of the bed.

"We've had a good run, haven't we?" Mr. X said, looking at Cathy.

"We have, Mr. X," Cathy said.

"I don't have much left in the tank," he said between difficult breaths. "I poured myself into my work at the expense of everything else. I sacrificed a lot. And so did my family," he acknowledged, smiling forlornly at the women on either side of him. "I was able to do more for humanity as a businessman than I ever could as a husband or father. Even though it meant shortchanging those close to me. I feel terrible about that, but it was how I was able to be most useful. As painful as it is to say,

I wouldn't change anything." Mary and Helen exchanged a quick, pained look over the top of his head.

"Wherever life takes you... follow your inner scorecard..." he whispered. It wasn't clear if he was speaking to me or everyone, but I took it to heart.

Those were his last words before he slipped quietly out of consciousness. His wife and daughter sat by the bed and gently stroked his hands. Mr. X couldn't speak, but he still held onto their hands as a sign of life. Mary caressed his head, "If you want to go, it's OK. You can go, Dad." Tears now streamed down Mary's cheeks. Helen whispered something in his ear--a final message from wife to husband.

"I love you, Daddy," Mary said. "I always will."

At that moment, Mr. X smiled. His face relaxed and his grasp loosened.

He was gone.

CHAPTER 38

I don't remember walking out of the hospital, but I found myself outside. The sun was fully radiant--a glorious day in Wichita that stood in stark contrast to the dense mental fog I was swimming in.

I wandered the streets, not knowing where I was or where I was going. The tears streamed down my face. I avoided eye contact with strangers, sure they figured me for a lunatic but unable to care. I kept walking and crying uncontrollably.

How do people deal with losing someone important to them? I felt hopeless, rudderless, defeated. My mind spun at a thousand RPM yet went nowhere.

How was I going to make good on my promises to Mr. X? *I hadn't learned enough. My mentor was gone before we could finish our lessons. How was I going to write this book?*

I was defeated and I knew it.

A buzzing in my pocket broke my trance. I blinked the tears out of my eyes. It was a voicemail from my parents. They wanted to know if I had any extra cash that I could send to help make the next mortgage payment. *Impeccable timing, guys.* Eventually I caught a cab and found myself on the next standby flight to California. There weren't any answers left for me in Wichita.

CHAPTER 39

It turned out there were no answers waiting for me back in California either, just more grief. I opened the front door to the apartment and found a bag sitting accusingly in the center of the entryway. Inside the bag I found a few sets of clothes and my toiletries neatly packed. On top of the bag was a note from Stephanie. It said we needed some time apart and that I should think about my priorities. *When it rains, it pours.*

I called Larry and asked if I could crash on his couch while I tried to extinguish the dumpster fire of my life. He was his usual amiable self and invited me without hesitation. I hung up and wandered the apartment aimlessly. *Our* apartment. I was hit with a flood of memories. Funny moments. Fights. More good than bad. I thought about what Mr. X had said about not letting her get away. Was it already too late? Was she already gone?

I flopped miserably on the couch and glanced at the coffee table, strewn with folders, notebooks, and printed out journal articles. It was a stabbing reminder that I'd never find another girl as smart as Steph. I picked up the top one and mindlessly read the title: *Clinical Versus Mechanical Prediction: A Meta-Analysis.* The words barely registered, but for some unknown reason I kept reading:

> *On average, mechanical-prediction techniques were about 10% more accurate than clinical predictions. Superiority for mechanical-prediction techniques was consistent, regardless of the judgment task, type of judges, judges' amounts of experience, or the types of data being combined.* ***These data indicate that mechanical predictions of human behaviors are equal or superior to clinical prediction methods for a wide range of circumstances.***

An idea tickled at my subconscious. I could feel the build up of mental static, like a bolt of lightning about to crack the sky. I was onto something, but I needed to pull at the thread. I tucked her article under my arm and took off for the library, my sad bag of belongings in tow.

CHAPTER 40

The next week flew by as I prepped for my fateful board meeting presentation. I desperately needed this Big Rock promotion to help me dig out of my Grand-Canyon-sized life hole and buy some time to write Mr. X's book. I needed a lucky break, but as the genius behind McDonald's, Ray Kroc, once said, "The more you sweat, the luckier you get," so sweat I did. *Imagine a montage of me hustling at work by day, buried under a mountain of books at the library, pouring through psychology research, and grabbing a few winks on Larry's couch before waking up to do it all again the next day. End montage.*

I tried the safer back-channel of small talk text messages with Stephanie. She wasn't having it. She didn't seem that eager for reconciliation at the moment.

The afternoon of the Big Rock presentation arrived. Presenters were randomly assigned time slots, and wouldn't you know it, I was going right after Vance. *FML.* Word around the office was that he was working on something transformative. No one knew the full details, but it involved machine-learning and neural networks that would change everything we did at Big Rock. He had artificial intelligence that was accurate out to the fourth decimal place. A rumor was circulating that he'd personally hired outside expert consultants and AI researchers from Carnegie Mellon to help him with his presentation. *Probably more accurately, his father had hired them, but why sweat the details?* I didn't even know what half of those words meant.

I showed up to the boardroom fifteen minutes before my scheduled time, my stomach in a familiar knot. Vance's presentation was just letting out. I caught a snippet of two higher-ups conversing as they passed.

"Wow, that was on a whole different level. That guy will probably be our boss soon."

"Yeah, I feel sorry for the poor schlub who's presenting next." *I've been called worse.*

Vance emerged triumphant and was immediately surrounded by colleagues who appeared just in time to slap him on the back. After a few minutes, I was looking for the ref to throw the flag for excessive celebration. Eventually the clingers disbursed and Vance walked over to me.

"Oh, you're presenting today?" he said. "I figured you would have been in Wichita burying an old man." My stomach knot dissolved in a bath of hot acid. He smiled knowing he was getting to me and pressed on. "I'm not sure why you're even bothering. I've already got this in the bag. But I guess losers always think they have a chance, don't they?" He winked at me as he strutted off. *Where's a random lightning bolt when you need one?*

The Big Rock higher-ups were filtering back into the room. Normally this would have been the last chance to do my customary dry heave in the bathroom. Yet a feeling of calmness washed over me. Little did Vance know, I had an ace up my sleeve.

CHAPTER 41

Around the boardroom table sat a familiar collection of middle-aged men and women in business suits. The Big Rock management team--different, yet somehow all the same.

I silently stared around the room, making purposeful individual eye contact before I started speaking. *Command the Room* was tip number four in an article I had read, "10 Hacks For a Killer Presentation."

I cleared my throat and started my PowerPoint. "Baseball drafts. Medical diagnosis. University admissions. Wine pricing. Criminal recidivism. Measuring brain damage. What do these all have in common?" I paused for effect. My audience gave me nothing in return. "They're all domains where a simple model beats the so-called experts. The evidence is clear: quantitative models provide a ceiling, which us humans subtract from, not a floor on which we build upon."

At least the puzzled faces around the table weren't buried in their phones. They were confused, but I had their attention.

"America's pastime," I said, turning to a slide with a picture of a baseball player. "Professional athletes have a certain look. Baseball scouts know a good player when they see one in action. They can feel it in their gut; some guys just have it. Then along came Billy Beane, the General Manager of the Oakland A's. He started looking at numbers, not if the player had 'the look.' He stopped caring if the prospect seemed athletic. He keyed in on the player's on-base and slugging percentages. To Beane, the numbers didn't lie. He ignored his team's internal scouting recommendations. He didn't even want to know what a player looked like for fear it would taint his impression of the numbers. He had created a simple quant model for what made for a good baseball player. He was leaving his gut feelings out and trusting the numbers. Guess what? It worked. In 2002, the Oakland A's won 103 games, including an unheard of twenty straight. All this success came against teams whose payrolls were three times bigger. Michael Lewis wrote the best-seller *Moneyball* about the triumph of Billy Beane and the Oakland A's. Can you imagine the temerity of trusting simple numbers over scores of well-paid, lifelong baseball experts?"

The shift in body language in the room told me they were interested. Behind me I put up a slide with a picture of a handsome, competent-looking man clad in scrubs. *Paging Dr. McDreamy.*

"I have something disturbing to tell you. Researchers asked doctors the seven most important factors to determine if an ulcer is malignant or benign. Size, shape, location, etc. Very basic stuff for any doctor. The researchers then developed a simple model based on the doctors' answers. It was stupidly simple--too basic to be of use. The researchers then asked the doctors to look at ninety-six different individual stomach ulcers and score them on a scale from "definitely malignant" to "definitely benign." Here's where it gets interesting. Without telling the doctors, the researchers mixed in duplicates at random so that the doctors actually saw each ulcer slide twice. Sneaky, right?"

"It turns out, the simple model proved to be extremely good at predicting benign versus malignant. And the experts? The doctors' diagnoses were all over the map. First, the experts didn't agree with each other. That's not surprising--experts have conflicting opinions all the time. Here's the crazy part: when presented slides of the same ulcer in duplicate, every doctor ended up contradicting themselves. *The experts couldn't even agree with themselves!* The stupid little model outperformed not only the average doctor in the group, it outperformed the single best doctor's score! If your life was on the line, you'd want the dumb model, not this handsome fellow behind me making your diagnosis."

I saw a few people shaking their heads in disbelief. I pushed on.

"How many of you have high school-aged kids?" A smattering of hands went up. "You might appreciate this one." Behind me the slide flashed to a hopeful youth in cap and gown.

"Some college admissions require a panel interview. Students prep witty anecdotes and and rattle off lists of their extracurriculars. But there's a problem: repeat studies have found interview scoring has no correlation with graduation rates. If the purpose of the interview was to predict who could cut the mustard in college, the results aren't good. The interviews are completely worthless. A simple model ranking the students' test scores has greater predictive value. So what's the point of the expert interviews?"

"Million-dollar baseball contracts, cancer rates, and college admission are all life-changing events. Let's get into something a little more fun. Specifically, the pricing of Bordeaux wines. I've been to the Big Rock Gala and I know we appreciate wine around here." This elicited a few grins. Behind me, the slide showed a verdant winery bathed in French sunset.

"Researchers developed a simple four-factor equation to predict the price of Bordeaux wines. They used the age of the vintage, the average temperature during the growing season, and two separate rainfall measurements that are key during the grapes' growth cycle. That's it. And yet, that model explained 83% of the variation in pricing. The model routinely beat the snobby experts' predictions."

"Back to the serious. Hopefully something none of us have to face: parole." Behind me a picture of a man in an orange jumpsuit stood before a panel of frowning judges.

"The justice system tries to prevent parolees from committing another crime and winding up back in prison. This failure goes by the fancy name 'criminal recidivism.' A study in the Pennsylvania corrections system created a simple model based on just three factors. One, the type of offense. Two, the number of past convictions. Three, the number of violations of prison rules. Very obvious measurements of rehabilitation. This "dumb" three-factor model ended up being nearly four times as accurate at predicting recidivism than the parole board filled with expert judges. Having the parolee go before a panel served no purpose."

"Fun side note: other studies have found that you are anywhere between two- and six-times as likely to be released if you're one of the first three cases considered during the day when compared to the last three. The reason? The judge is likely hungry or tired. At least the simple model doesn't get hangry. If you're ever on trial for something, ask for the earliest possible slot." *Knowing the scruples of Big Rock, it wasn't impossible this would be relevant information for some of them.*

"Back to medicine. Researchers developed a simple rules-based test that assessed intellectual deficits due to brain damage. The model correctly identified eighty-three percent of new out-of-sample cases. Pretty solid hit rate. How did the experts do? Unfortunately, experienced professionals working from the same data only scored with fifty-eight percent accuracy, dramatically underperforming the model. It gets worse for our beloved experts. Groups of *inexperienced* professionals given the same data scored sixty-three percent, beating the experienced cohort. The researchers attributed this bizarre finding to the experienced professionals overconfidence in their own judgment. Good thing we don't have too many experts in this room, right?," I said. The group laughed nervously, probably assuming I wasn't referring to them personally. *We're always the exception.*

"There's another wrinkle to this story. A follow-up medical study gave the doctors the results of the model as part of their data to aid decision-making. The humans knew the model had scored better than they did. They took a similar test with this new information. Access to the model did improve their scores, but the humans still underperformed the simple model on its own. They *still* thought they could add something helpful to the model's results. Instead, they subtracted. Let me repeat that: even when given the model's results, the experts still underperformed."

Heads were shaking in disbelief.

"As painful as it is to admit, the evidence is damning. A simple, quantitative model represents a ceiling in performance that us humans subtract from, and not a floor onto which we can build. The simple model just keeps beating us again and again."

I gave them a few quiet beats to contemplate the implications.

"Perhaps you think I'm cherry-picking studies where models are the clear winners? Sadly, I'm not. Researchers conducted a meta-analysis of 136 studies where experts squared off against simple models. I'm glad you're all sitting down before I tell you the results. In sixty-four of the studies, the simple model was the clear winner. In another sixty-four studies, the model and the experts were basically tied. That leaves just eight studies where the experts beat the simple model. Eight out of 136."

A new slide appeared behind me. Even though I knew it was a cardinal sin of presenting, I read the quote on the slide directly to the group.

"There is no controversy in social science which shows such a large body of qualitatively diverse studies coming out so uniformly in the same direction as this one... predicting everything from the outcomes of football games to the diagnosis of liver disease--when you can hardly come up with a half a dozen studies showing even a weak tendency in favor of the clinician, it is time to draw a practical conclusion."
- Paul Meehl, Professor of Psychology at the University of Minnesota

"I hope I've belabored the point enough to prove that simple models perform better than experts across a range of domains. So… what does this mean for Big Rock? What should we do with this information?"

Crickets.

"Here's one idea. When we evaluate a company for possible acquisition, we judge management on their capital allocations skills. We assess how well they make resource decisions. We look at how well they've grown their company. We decide if we're going to keep them or axe them. It's very much like a job interview. Or a parole board review. Or a baseball tryout." *Drawing the parallels yet?*

"You can see where I'm going with this. I've developed a simple model to judge management's capital allocation process. No more talking to the CEO and being wowed by their words. You can't hide from the simple model and the scorecard."

The room was deathly silent, like outer-space. I could see a handful of now indignant faces in the audience. When it was doctors and baseball scouts, it made sense that the models performed better. But their domain was different. They were *true* experts at judging management. And experts don't like being called out.

"I have a Warren Buffett quote for you that summarizes this entire presentation." Behind me on the screen was a short quote:

> *"Paradoxically, when 'dumb' money acknowledges its limitations, it ceases to be dumb."*
>
> *-- Warren Buffett*

"I don't mean this disrespectfully, but I can guarantee you my simple model will outperform our committee of experts in evaluating managerial talent. The odds are too much in my favor."

Well, it's now or never. I let out a dramatic sigh. "Now comes the difficult part of the presentation. I'm going to tell you what you'll use as excuses for why Big Rock can't implement a simple model like this. And after that, I'm going to tell you the *real* reason why Big Rock will reject this obviously superior system." *Crickets in outer-space.*

"First, you'll say everyone else *thinks* they're an expert, but we're *actually* experts. We're the exception. OK... but did you go to eight years of intensive schooling, then several more years of formalized residency and fellowship to learn your craft? Because the doctors in the studies did. It takes an average of 40,000 hours of training to become a doctor. They thought they were the exceptions as well, and they got trounced by the simple models. So think hard before you assume you're the exception."

"Second, you'll say that this doesn't apply to our industry. Evaluating capital allocation skills is too complicated for a simple model." I paused to build a little suspense. "It's not. In fact, a simple model performs best under the following conditions..."

Behind me the slide changed to read:

Simple models thrive when…
- the problem is ill-structured and complex.
- the information is incomplete, ambiguous, and changing.
- the goals are ill-defined, shifting, or competing.
- the stress is high, due to time constraints and/or high stakes.
- decisions rely upon an interaction with others.

"Don't all of these conditions look familiar?" The faces staring back at me bore countenances that ranged from skepticism to hostility.

"You'll say our current system is working just fine, why do we need to change it? I understand the force of corporate inertia is very strong. But if we want to be the industry leaders, heck, even *rebels*, don't we need to set the standard and think differently? As Sir John Templeton said, 'The time to reflect on your investing methods is when you are most successful, not when you are making the most mistakes.'"

"Let's talk about the *real* reasons why you won't adopt the simple model." *Awkward didn't even begin to describe the silence.*

"First, following a simple model would mean no longer needing a committee to evaluate. There's a lot of ego and power wrapped up in being a trusted expert and decision-maker. Who wants to admit a stupid model does a better job than they do? No one in this room. Or any boardroom for that matter. As Upton Sinclair remarked, 'It is difficult to get a man to understand something, when his salary depends upon his not understanding it.'"

"Furthermore, following a simple model is a tough sell. The model won't be perfect. Nothing is. It will make mistakes, though all the research suggests it will make fewer than a human. But as soon as the model makes a mistake, everyone looking from the outside will scoff and say, 'You let that crummy little model decide for you? *Are you daft?!* What did you expect was going to happen?' It will be hard to stick to the model and not cave to pressure. We feel safe when we do what everyone else is doing and stay with the herd. Being a rebel requires great strength. As John Maynard Keynes quipped, 'Worldly wisdom teaches that it is better for reputation to fail conventionally than to succeed unconventionally.'"

"But…" *Let's pause to build that drama.*

"...what if…" *Little bit more.*

"…what if you could put your ego aside and acknowledge that you might be *dumb money*, to use Mr. Buffett's term? What if the ultimate expertise was knowing when to stand down?"

"Here's my suggestion: keep the committee. Use the model as a secret weapon, like a hidden black box. Trust what it comes up with and pretend it was your expertise that found the right answer. Then spend the rest of your time golfing and congratulating yourselves for outsmarting everyone. But *do not* make the common mistake of trying to modify what the model comes up with because you believe you know better. You don't. At least that claim is not supported by any of the research."

"Any questions?"

Career suicide achieved.

CHAPTER 42

It probably won't surprise you to hear the Big Rock higher-ups didn't have any immediate questions. The silence was excruciating. Finally, one of them asked if I could step outside while they conferred. I closed the door behind me and sat on a bench near the door. They were going to fire me for calling them out. These aren't people who appreciate being challenged. They do the challenging. Normally these dire circumstances would have my mind racing a million miles an hour with swirling visions of living under a bridge, destitute and alone.

Yet I was strangely calm. I was a man who had accepted his fate and awaited his turn at the gallows. There was no protest required--nothing more to say. I would die with dignity.

It felt like I'd been sitting on the bench with my thoughts for an hour. I glanced at my phone and only ten minutes had passed. The doors reopened and I was invited back in.

The group shot leary looks my way as I re-entered and stood before them. Finally, one of them spoke. "Your presentation was very… *unique*. It's not often that someone speaks so frankly to us. Apparently you must have felt like you had nothing to lose to be so brash?"

Oh, boy. Here comes the guillotine.

"And yet some of us found your idea of trusting a simple model to be something worth exploring in the future. Maybe not your exact implementation, but the concept was mildly interesting."

"Thank you," I mumbled. *Mildly interesting--that's it?*

"However, we don't think it's right for Big Rock at this time." *Figures.*

"I understand," I said. "I guess this means I'm fired?"

"Fired? No, actually quite the opposite. We've agreed that you won the analyst promotion. We could use more independent thinkers around here." Some of the higher-ups looked at each other and smiled, proud of their benevolence. A few looked considerably less pleased--I guess they had been outvoted?

What?! I was about to get fired, and now they're telling me I got the promotion? That I was in for a major pay raise? *And that I beat Vance?* Jeez, how much of my life had I wasted in worry? Worrying about things that never came to be. Why was I in my own head so much? What was I leaving on the table by caving to crushing internal doubts?

In that instant, something inside me changed. *That was it. Never again.*

I spoke with a new rush of confidence, "Ladies and gentlemen, thank you very much for your time. And thank you for the offer of the promotion. It's a very kind gesture."

They nodded approvingly.

"However, I have to decline." *So much for the nodding.*

"In fact, I'm offering my resignation, effective immediately. I believe in my simple model. So much so that I have to pursue the idea farther. Maybe I'll start my own investment fund that identifies good capital allocators by scoring them with a simple model. And I already have the name: *The Rebel Allocator Fund.*"

I saw nothing but looks of confusion. It's not often you see someone transform before your eyes. I was a new person. I knew in an instant that I didn't want to win their game or climb their ladder. I wanted to be useful in my own unique way. I was destined to make a bigger dent in the universe than anything Big Rock could offer.

"Someone very wise once told me to follow my own inner scorecard. Now if you'll excuse me, there's a girl I need to keep from becoming the one that got away."

I didn't look back as I glided out of the room, a man with a singular purpose.

I called Stephanie as soon as I was outside the Big Rock building. She answered with a sigh and a "What do you want?" *Ouch.*

Before we could get derailed, I told her she had to meet me at the special place of our first hike at sunrise tomorrow morning. The energy in my voice must have been just enough to sway her. She agreed to come, though she was reluctant. It didn't matter. She said yes, which meant I still had a chance. We hung up before I could fumble the ball.

I had a date with the jeweler and a hardware store.

CHAPTER 43

The air was chill in the mountains. The stream babbled quietly as the birds awoke and chirped their morning greetings. Nature, at her most pristine. The dark sky was slow to relinquish the twinkling stars to the coming sunrise. I needed to be there early to pull this off.

I had barely slept, and not just because Larry's couch was like a torture device. *My god, how many crossbars in the back are required before it breaks some Geneva Convention codes?* Yet I couldn't have been more wide awake. The sun crested the mountain range and bathed the entire scene in a soft radiance.

My eyes were fixed on the trail she'd be coming up. I shifted my weight from foot to foot, both to release a little nervous energy and because I was cold. It wasn't working much for either.

Just when I started to feel the darkness of doubt creep in, Stephanie emerged from a grove of trees. A cold hand reached down through me and grabbed my stomach. I smiled and waved like I was flagging her down in a crowded train station. *We're the only two humans within a twenty-five-mile radius, dummy.*

Her hair was drawn back and her makeup light. She wore a red checkered flannel that was tied in a knot in the front over a white ribbed tank top, tan shorts, long wool socks, and her familiar hiking boots. She looked like she'd stepped right out of the Patagonia catalog of my dreams.

"Hi," I started.

"Hi," she replied flatly. *Still cold.*

"I've missed you," I said.

"You have?" she said. "I wasn't sure you'd even noticed, you've been so busy."

"I know. I'm sorry I've been pulled in so many different directions. I've been struggling to keep up."

"How's Mr. X?" she asked.

"He... passed away," I could barely say. Fresh tears found their way out.

"Oh, my god, Nick. I'm so sorry," she said.

"Thank you," I said. "He made a big impression on me. I'm just happy I got to see him one last time before he passed."

"It's a good thing you left when you did then. I'm sorry I was being so dramatic. I just felt so disconnected from you. I wanted to know what you were feeling. Plus my parents were in my head. I had a hunch that you might propose that weekend. And when I realized it wasn't going to happen, I didn't do a very good job hiding my disappointment. I wasn't the best version of myself. I'm really sorry."

"How was the rest of Catalina?" I asked.

"Not good without you there," she said.

I smiled. "I have something to show you. It's just up the river a bit. I made you something."

"You did?" she said with a smile. "I do love surprises."

We hiked upstream for a few minutes. I took her hand as she stepped over a small tree that had fallen across the trail. It felt good to touch her again, even in that small way.

"I need you to put this blindfold on now."

"What?"

"Just trust me," I said.

I tied a scarf around her face to cover her eyes. I took her hand and lead her around the bend. I guided her up the side of a boulder that was nestled near the trail. When we got to the top, I stood behind her and removed the blindfold. She blinked her eyes and looked out.

"Oh my god, Nick." Tears started to streamed down her face. From our elevated position on the boulder, she could see at least two dozen places where I'd stenciled in red paint "Will you marry me?" on the exposed rock faces. She turned to find me bent down on one knee.

"Stephanie... I know things have been difficult. But I've come to some realizations."

"You have?" she said.

"Yes, Mr. X told me after he met you that I'd be a fool to let you get away," I said. "And he was right."

"I knew I liked him for some reason," she said.

"Steph, I've changed in ways I'm not sure I can describe. I quit my job at Big Rock."

"What?!"

"I had to," I said. "I wasn't happy there--I didn't fit in. If I stayed, I would have become a shell of myself. But I have a new path I'm excited to walk down. Like, crazy excited. I can't wait to tell you all about it. And I want to walk this new path with you. Only you." I paused, for dramatic effect and mostly because of the enormous lump in my throat. "Stephanie, will you marry me?" I opened a small box to reveal an exceptionally modest ring. *Even then I'd be making payments on it for eternity. Yet I knew it was the best capital allocation decision I'd ever make.*

"Yes, Nick. Of course I will," she said through tears.

I stood up and we kissed. I soaked in the moment, imagining how I'd tell our grandchildren about it. *I'm still working on that whole "being present" thing.*

As we exited off the big boulder, I grabbed a bag I'd tucked into the bushes earlier.

"Being married to me will probably never be easy," I said. "I'll make a big mess, but my heart will always be in the right place. And that starts right now, even while we're engaged." I handed her a brush and a wad of steel wool and smiled. "We've got my first mess to clean up."

It took us three hours of intense scrubbing to remove the red paint from all of the rocks. *Welcome to betrothed bliss, Steph.*

EPILOGUE

Last I heard, Vance had been fired from BR. The story was he had been accused of sexual harassment by a coworker. *Not a shocker.* The first to step forward broke the seal and a dozen others came forward. Even Vance's rich father couldn't hold back that avalanche. It came to light that Vance had been falsifying numbers on practically every assignment he'd worked on, including his miraculous presentation that wowed the higher-ups.

Not long after, I visited the coffee shop where Steph used to sling caffeine, for old time's sake. My eyes widened when I recognized the barista—it was Vance! I kept it classy, not wanting to gloat at his shift in fortune. I did ask him for some extra straws though; I was working on an important business problem.

I'm happy to report my father landed a series of important (non-pro-bono) cases and my mom took a position at a charitable foundation focusing on the environment. They still tilted at windmills, but their financial struggles were soon behind them. *For now.* I hope they learned an important lesson about saving when they can, not when they have to.

Relations with Steph's parents improved after it became apparent I had set a decisive course in life. *It's amazing what a little confidence will do.* I can't blame them for worrying about their daughter becoming stranded in the doldrums of the old version of myself. Her father shoots me words of encouragement now instead of icy daggers.

* * *

I got a note from Mr. X in the mail. I was shocked and confused at first, until I noticed it had been postmarked weeks before. He had sent it before my last trip out to Wichita. It must have gotten lost in the mail and just resurfaced. A tear streamed down as I opened it. It warmed my heart to see one last Warren Buffett quote from Mr. X:

> *"The heads of many companies are not skilled in capital allocation. Their inadequacy is not surprising. Most bosses rise to the top because they have excelled in an area such as marketing, production, engineering, administration or, sometimes, institutional politics.*
>
> *Once they become CEOs, they face new responsibilities. They now must make capital allocation decisions, a critical job that they may have never tackled and that is not easily mastered. To stretch the point, it's as if the final step for a highly-talented musician was not to perform at Carnegie Hall but, instead, to be named Chairman of the Federal Reserve. In the end, plenty of unintelligent capital allocation takes place in corporate America."*

Do what you can to make your dent, son.

- Mr. X

I will, Mr. X. You have my word.

* * *

A few months after the lost note surfaced, I received a call from Cathy:

"Hi, Nick. How are you?"

"I'm doing well, thanks. And you?"

"It's been a little rough around here after losing Mr. X, but his successor is a wonderful leader, so the business is in good hands. Mr. X thought it might run better without him. I won't say that's true, but we're doing just fine."

"That's good to hear."

"How's Stephanie?"

"She's great. We're actually engaged now."

"Oh, that's terrific news! I'm so happy-- you two are a good match."

"I tried to screw it up, but we've figured things out. You're definitely on our wedding invite list."

"I wouldn't miss it!"

"Did I tell you that I left Big Rock?"

"No, is leaving a good thing or a bad thing?"

"It's a good thing. Mostly. I didn't fit in there and although the paycheck was desperately needed, I was selling my soul to earn it. I had to get out, even though it means a financial struggle for the foreseeable future. I'm actually starting my own thing instead, if you can believe that. I know, it's a crazy thought: Mr. Socialism starts his own business."

"No, I love it. That's so great. It's funny, I thought we'd be having this conversation years from now."

"What?"

"Let me explain. In Mr. X's will, he left you a sum of money that was only available if you started your own business. He said specifically that he wanted to leave you enough where you could afford to do anything, but not so much that you could afford to do nothing." I started to tear up. That specific language meant Mr. X thought of me as his son. It took me a few moments to gain my composure. Cathy understood the implication and waited patiently.

"How did he know I'd ever want to start my own business?" I finally said.

"He was very wise and knew you were destined to be your own boss at some point. Plus, he knew you didn't fit in at Big Rock. It was just a matter of time."

"He was very wise. I miss him."

"We all do."

"I feel like we didn't get a chance to finish our lessons. Like our time was cut short."

"I think Mr. X would say you learned everything you needed to learn."

"That does sound like him."

"Well, I should probably get back to work here. I'll have Mr. X's lawyer contact you regarding the details of the inheritance soon."

"OK, thank you, Cathy. I should get back to work also. And Cathy…"

"Yes, Nick?"

"You have my word that the book I write about Mr. X will be worthy of the original source. It will be something he'd be proud of."

"I know you will, Nick."

THE REBEL ALLOCATOR'S CHECKLIST

- [ ] Respect the Iron Law of Economic Survival: Cost < Price < Value.
- [ ] Value is perceived by the customer, focus on what doesn't change for them, engineering doesn't always have the right answer because of the customer's subjective perception.
- [ ] Small, incremental improvements really add up.
- [ ] Push decision-making down as close to the customer as possible.
- [ ] Choose your strategy: differentiated product or lowest-cost producer?
- [ ] Appreciate the tradeoffs between profit and brand. Are you storing fat or glucose?
- [ ] Practice zero-based budgeting.
- [ ] Strategic costs delight the customer and build a moat around your business. Invest in them.
- [ ] Non-strategic costs sap your resources and should be eliminated.
- [ ] Don't "paint the fourth wall."
- [ ] Cash is the oxygen of business. Don't cut it close.
- [ ] Fund strategies, not individual projects.
- [ ] Returns on invested capital tell you if you're providing value. It's your weight-lifting form. Only add the plates of growth when you can maintain good form.
- [ ] Growth isn't necessarily good or bad, it's just "more."
- [ ] Be patient like the pine cone. Everything moves in cycles.

- [ ] Be confident to zig when everyone else is zagging.
- [ ] Lay out all of your capital allocation options into a single menu before you decide.
- [ ] Keep your balance sheet conservative. One of your responsibilities is to serve as an economic shock absorber and protect various stakeholders.
- [ ] Imagine all the different ways to "put a roof over your head."
- [ ] Perform the 11-Star Experience exercise to push the boundaries of what's possible to delight customers.
- [ ] Don't do mergers and acquisitions for the BBQ Factor, don't expect synergy miracles.
- [ ] Using shares for M&A is like selling part of your business. Get back at least as much value as you're giving up. Chances are, you're overpaying.
- [ ] The dumbest activity occurs late in the cycle. Tread carefully.
- [ ] Be conservative with healthy margins of safety on all projections.
- [ ] If you can't create value by reinvesting in operations, M&A, or creating a new business line, you should return capital to shareholders.
- [ ] You have a fiduciary responsibility to your shareholders to keep your stock trading as close to intrinsic value as possible. This helps prevent incoming and outgoing shareholders from taking advantage of each other.
- [ ] Having publicly traded shares are like having your own currency. Respect them as such.
- [ ] Use share buybacks to put a floor under your stock. You never know why a partner needs liquidity.

- [ ] Tell your partners/shareholders everything you'd want to know if your roles were reversed so they can arrive at their own fair value of the company.

- [ ] Paying a dividend should be a last resort.

- [ ] Never forget you are a fiduciary for your shareholders. Treat them like partners.

- [ ] Thoughtful allocation of resources is one of the most important societal functions entrusted to you. It's important for customers, employees, boards, management, and the environment. Give it your best effort.

For more Rebel Allocator resources, please visit: www.fivegoodquestions.co/rebel-resources.

There you'll find printable versions of The Rebel Allocator's Checklist, Capital Allocation Base Rates, an extensive bibliography and relevant white papers.

You can also sign up to receive occasional email updates on rebellious capital allocation, if you're weird like me and love this stuff.

CAPITAL ALLOCATION BASE RATES

If you're going to be a rebel allocator, it doesn't hurt to know what businesses have historically done as your starting point. Always remember you can deviate when logical reasoning says you should; the crowd isn't necessarily right.

Trust your judgment.

Sources and Uses of Cash for Large Cap US Companies 1990-2018**

Sources of Cash	
Operating Cash Flow	59%
Debt Issuance	23%
Equity Issuance	5%
Other	5%
Working Capital Changes	4%
Investment Sales	3%
Sale of Property, Plant, and Equipment	1%

Uses of Cash	
Capital Expenditures	25%
Debt Paydown	20%
Buybacks	12%
Research and Development	9%
Acquisitions	8%
Dividends	8%
Working Capital Changes	7%
Investments	6%
Other	5%

** Data used with permission from O'Shaughnessey Asset Management

ACKNOWLEDGEMENTS

First, I recognize there are thousands of great books that come out every year. It means a lot to me that you chose to spend time with mine. If you found this story worthwhile, I have two favors to ask, both with the goal of getting the book's lessons into more hands and closing the capital allocation gap Mr. Buffett describes.

The first favor would be to leave a review on amazon (or goodreads). Stars are the currency of books these days and the ratings impact the algorithms. More votes lead to more recommendations and exposure. Your review, good or bad, is welcome. The second favor would be to get a copy of the book into the hands of any CEOs or boards of directors you think could benefit. Capital allocation occurs throughout the org chart, so leadership at any level would likely get something useful from the story you just read.

You won't find an original idea of mine in this book. (Well, except for Nick's proposal to Stephanie—I pulled that one off in real life.) Everything intelligent is borrowed from people smarter than myself. First and foremost, I want to thank Warren Buffett for the intellectual generosity of his writing and speaking. As a first-year MBA, I had the opportunity to travel to Omaha for a Q&A session and lunch with Mr. Buffett. Talk about a game-changer! Charlie Munger is also one of my heroes and I've been lucky to enough to catch the Warren and Charlie Show in person for more than a dozen years during the Berkshire weekend in Omaha. Both of their fingerprints are all over this book; it simply doesn't exist without them. I avoided direct attributions to keep from breaking the flow of the story, but Mr. X's most sage quotes are often directly cribbed from Warren and Charlie. They deserve all the credit.

I also have thank yous for specific ideas: James Clear on the power of one percent improvements. Yvon Chouinard for the concept of yarak. Gary Keller for the importance of focusing on ONE thing. 3G Capital for zero-based budgeting. Bob Fifer for strategic versus non-strategic expenses and differentiated product versus lowest cost producer. Tom Murphy for the story of painting only three walls. Nick Gogerty for inspiring the Iron Law of Economic Survival. Various Austrian economists throughout history for the theory of subjective value and non-homogenous capital accumulation. Al Ries and Jack Trout for the Law of Duality. Jeff Bezos for focusing on delighting customers with things that are unlikely to change. Rory Sutherland for the six billion dollar London to Paris train example and the flower-weed advertising joke. Noted Air Force pilot John Boyd for the German concept of auftragstaktik. Nassim Taleb for the Lindy effect. Peter Thiel for thoughts on monopoly. Jason Fung for inspiring the comparison to insulin in the body with profit versus brand tradeoffs. Sardar Biglari for operational leverage in the restaurant industry, the economics of franchising, and buying back your own restaurant roofs. Elliot Noss for net promoter score and for more generally being a top-flight capital allocator. Michael Mauboussin for clearing up the concepts of return on invested capital, research on mergers and acquisitions, strategies vs. projects, and seminal white papers on capital allocation (he's the best). Mark Spitznagel for the roundabout strategy of the pinecone. Edward Chancellor for capital cycle theory. John Tobin for the Q ratio and the buy versus build calculus. Brian Chesky for the eleven-star customer experience. Barry Schwartz for the paradox of choice. McKinsey for their various articles on zero-based budgeting. Andrew Lawrence and Mark Thornton for the skyscraper index. Ben Graham for thoughts on treating shareholders with respect. David Foster Wallace for the two fishes in water joke. James

Montier for his clever writing and research on simple models versus experts. O'Shaughnessey Asset Management for the data on sources and uses of corporate cash.

On the specifics of the writing process and story construction, I owe a debt of gratitude to the following books: Stephen King's *On Writing*, William Zinsser's *On Writing Well*, Anne Lamott's *Bird by Bird*, Steven Pressfield's *The War of Art*, Blake Snyder's *Save the Cat*, John McPhee's *Draft No. 4*, Ryan Holiday's *Perennial Seller*, and Dave Chilton for his top notch course on book marketing for self-publishers.

On a personal note, my family (and most notably my wife) put up with a lot in the multi-year process of writing this book. Authorship can be a soul-grinding roller coaster. I apologize that I had to cash in so many chips to get this project done. And thanks for your excellent edits, hon! Thank you to my mom for using your proofreading superpowers.

Thank you to Lonnie Rush, Toby Carlisle, Mike McCoy, Bogie Baranowski, and Darren Virassammy for reading early drafts and providing helpful feedback. And a special thank you to Barbara Oakley who had the courage to tell me the early writing stunk (which it did!). You pointed me in the right direction and provided the necessary encouragement to make drastic improvements. You saved me so much embarrassment by being a good friend.

Made in the USA
Middletown, DE
13 May 2020